Mechanics, with its brightening and quickening of brain, will react on the other farm workers, and so our country will travel along the road to that millennium we see so clearly, but find so difficult to reach.
Selwyn Francis Edge

They'll a'ti cum doon a good bit in price afoor ah buys yan on 'em.
An unknown Yorkshire farmer

Two opinions on the arrival of the farm tractor, recorded in *The Motor* in 1917.

British International crawlers working on a farm in Warwickshire in October 1961. A 1960 BTD-8 ploughs with a Jumbotrac while a 1956 BTD-6 follows up with a set of Ransomes Baronet discs.

Tractors *in Britain*

Stuart Gibbard

Japonica Press

ISBN 0 9540222 1 1
UPC 69372700004 2

A catalogue record for this book is available from the British Library

Published by
Japonica Press
Low Green Farm, Hutton, Driffield,
East Yorkshire, YO25 9PX
United Kingdom

Cover design and book layout by Banks Design

Preface

There has been a great deal of romanticism attached to the age of the horse or steam on the farm, and the tractor has been reviled as a 'noisy and oily beast' by those who mourn the passing of the traditional ways of the land. However, the tractor has had a far greater impact on agriculture than either of the other two forms of motive power; it was the catalyst that brought about a change to intense mechanisation, improving production and heralding a new era of farming efficiency.

In the early days, farmers may have been reluctant to accept the tractor but once the move was made there was no turning back to the old methods. Who would want to walk behind a plough when you could ride in front of it, or start at five o'clock in the morning to get steam up for the day's work when you could have an engine that would (usually) burst instantaneously into life?

There are now many of us who appreciate that the tractor has a beauty all of its own. I will always remember going to a farm near Evesham a few years ago to film two Roadless 115 tractors in action for a video. We arrived early on a crisp autumn day to hear the machines beating up the hill towards us with some heavy cultivators in tow. Both tractors emerged from the morning mist, side by side, with their six-cylinder engines at full chat, exhausts streaming and headlights ablaze. Who could not fail to be moved by such a sight?

This book, then, is intended to be a celebration of the age of the tractor – a product of the twentieth century that in the space of 100 years has changed from a crude 'mechanical horse' to a machine at the cutting edge of twenty-first century technology. There are those that would argue that tractor development has actually gone beyond the needs of the average farmer, and that now is the time for manufacturers to step back and return to a more basic and affordable package. But it is not up to me to judge such political considerations; my task is to document what has gone before.

In no way is this book meant to be a history of the tractor; its aim is to illustrate how the concept of the tractor has changed in Britain, and how the face of farming has changed with it. I have tried to keep within the dateline of the twentieth century, and the first four and last two chapters chart the development of the tractor chronologically, while the middle chapters look more widely at its application and the affect it has had on dealers, farmers and drivers alike. I could have illustrated the changes in words, but I feel that contemporary photographs tell a better story. It is a concept that I began several years ago with my first book, *Tractors at Work*, and returning to it seems as comfortable as putting on a pair of old slippers.

It is impossible to put such a collection of photographs together without the help of many people. All those individuals and organisations who have kindly loaned images from personal, private or company archives are listed under the picture credits. I am very grateful to them all. Without them, this book would not have been possible.

I have reserved special thanks for Alan Salt, the editor of the Lincolnshire Free Press and the Spalding Guardian, and the chief photographer, Tim Wilson, for allowing me unprecedented access to their photographic archive. I must also thank Anna Oakford for her superb photographic work in making excellent prints from deteriorating negatives. I would like to express my gratitude to Jim Russell for permitting me to use several outstanding shots taken by his own camera; Ven Dodge for supplying many photograhs from both his own personal negative file and the Roadless collection; and Stephen Burtt who had the foresight to record his farm's history on film and was then kind enough to lend me his transparencies.

It is impossible to write a book of this scope without relying on the knowledge of others, and I would like to thank D. A. Davies (Robey Trust), Ray Hooley, Patrick Knight, Peter J. Longfoot, Peter Love, Mervyn Spokes and Ron Tibbs for their assistance with my research. I am especially grateful to the following three individuals for supplying both photographs and extensive information: James Baldwin, Robert Crawford and Derek Hackett.

I would also like to thank Peter Anderson (Trade Link), Michelle Covington-Jones (Exxon-Mobil), Ted Everett (AGCO), Alan Fuller (New Holland), Eileen Hockley (Ernest Doe), Eric May, Steve Mitchell (Pharo Communications), Stephen Perry (Perkins Engines), Shaun Preece, Clive Scattergood (Perkins Engines), Mike Teanby (BAGMA), Richard Whiskard (Four Seasons) and John-Paul Warner (Brookes & Vernons).

Finally, as usual, I must thank my wife, Sue, for help in making the final selection of photographs and laying out the pages, and my old friend and publisher, Stephen Moate, for his valuable input.

Introduction – The Rise and Fall of the British Tractor Industry

Britain has a rich heritage of industrial innovation, particularly in the field of agricultural engineering. Whether the country could claim to have invented the farm tractor is a contentious issue, but it certainly pioneered its development and spawned a tractor industry that was possibly second only to the USA.

The word tractor comes from the Latin verb *tractus* meaning *to pull*. It appeared towards the end of the nineteenth century and was used as a simple description for the 'pulling machines' that were found on the farm, and to mark the arrival of the internal combustion-powered prime-movers that were replacing the steam traction engines. In 1954, the British Standards Institute classified the term as 'a self-propelled power unit with wheels or tracks', while a modern dictionary entry refers to the tractor as 'a wheeled or tracked vehicle for using or pulling farm machinery.'

The tractor was not so much invented as more evolved out of two distinct lines of development. The early American tractors, and Hart Parr of Iowa always claimed to have been the first manufacturer to use the word *tractor* to describe its products, were no more than gasoline powered versions of the steam engines that were used for direct traction on the prairies. In Britain, the use of the steam traction engine was restricted mainly to threshing or cable cultivation while the draught animal remained the chief prime mover on the farm.

The motor car had replaced the horse on the roads, so it was only natural that many of the first attempts to harness the internal combustion engine for use on farms in the UK had automotive lineage and were little more than adapted road vehicles. This meant that the early British tractors, or 'agrimotors', were more compact than their heavier transatlantic cousins with their steam-inspired designs. The few larger machines that were built in Britain at the beginning of the century were designed for export or military rather than agricultural use.

The Ivel, built by Dan Albone of Biggleswade in Bedfordshire, appeared in 1902 and is generally considered to be the first practical British tractor. Other makes followed, and some manufacturers, such as Saunderson, survived for a time and enjoyed moderate success, but must most fell by the wayside as the demand for tractors remained low. While the British tractor industry remained in its infancy, production in the USA had increased steadily and development was on a much larger scale.

Several different types of American tractors were imported into Britain during the First World War as food production was stepped up in answer to the German U-boat

The Ivel is generally regarded as the first successful British tractor. Built at Biggleswade, it was introduced in 1902 and sold in reasonable numbers. This is an early example with trembler-coil ignition.

attacks on Allied shipping that were obstructing desperately needed food supplies. By 1916, there were around 5,000 tractors in the UK but it was not enough, as the call to arms had seriously deprived the farms of both men and horses. The situation was saved by an agreement reached with Henry Ford for him to supply the Ministry of Munitions with 5,000 of his Fordson tractors.

In 1919, Henry Ford opened a new plant at Cork in Ireland. It could be argued that this was the first tractor factory geared to mass production to be built on British soil, as at the time the country was still part of the United Kingdom and the establishment of the Irish Free State was still two years away. However, tractor production in mainland Britain remained sporadic through the 1920s with the depressed state of agriculture that had been brought about by the repeal of the Corn Protection Act in 1921. Austin and Rushton had both produced creditable machines, but financial pressure meant that both names had all but disappeared from the British market by 1930. For a time, it began to look as if the only new models of British tractors would be those produced by the established steam engine manufacturers such as Marshalls of Gainsborough and Fowlers of Leeds who could integrate tractor production with their other product lines.

Large-scale tractor production was finally established in Britain in 1932 after Ford moved its Fordson manufacturing facilities from Cork to its new plant at Dagenham in Essex. Another significant plant was opened four years later by David Brown at its Park Works near Huddersfield to build tractors for Harry Ferguson. By 1939, David Brown was making tractors under its own name from a new factory in the former United Thread Mills at Meltham.

The outbreak of the Second World War saw the country affected by another U-boat blockade leading to further food shortages. The government instigated a series of ploughing campaigns and the need for tractors was greater than ever. The Ford Motor Company rose to the challenge and produced over 137,000 tractors at its Dagenham plant between 1939 and 1945. This represented 95 per cent of all the wheeled tractors made in Britain during the war. This staggering amount was still not enough to meet the demand, and the UK production was supplemented by American machines imported from the USA under the lend-lease agreement. Britain entered the war with a population of only 52,000 tractors, but over 175,000 were working on its farms by 1944.

A 25-30 hp Saunderson tractor dating from around 1910. Herbert Saunderson was one of the most prolific early British manufacturers of farm tractors. He made a number of different models, and built up a significant export trade.

Ford introduced large-scale tractor production to Britain after its factory at Dagenham was opened in 1932. During the Second World War, the Dagenham plant built over 137,000 Fordsons, representing 95 per cent of the total UK wheeled tractor production.

For all farm work you need the reliability, economy and versatility of...

...Nuffield Universal with a **BMC DIESEL**

TWELVE MONTHS' WARRANTY

Backed by B.M.C. Service— the most comprehensive in Europe.

For range of optional extras see current Price List.

NUFFIELD UNIVERSAL

The 'FOUR' is powered by the famous B.M.C. 3.4 litre, 4-cylinder Diesel and the 'THREE' is built around the new 2.55 litre, 3-cylinder Diesel unit. High power output with fuel economy and absolute reliability are characteristic of both tractors, each model is widely adaptable to modern farming needs.

MORRIS MOTORS LTD. (AGRICULTURAL DIVISION), COWLEY, OXFORD. Overseas Business: Nuffield Exports Ltd., Oxford and 41-46 Piccadilly, W.1.

U. 148/C

A 1958 advertisement for Nuffield Universal 'Three' and 'Four' tractors. Nuffield was one of the many new names that appeared on the British market during the postwar period as more manufacturers moved into tractor and machinery manufacture to meet the growing demand from both at home and abroad.

British agriculture emerged from the war well equipped to cope with the postwar world food shortages. Many new farming methods and practices were in place but greater mechanisation was still needed to compensate for the limited manpower, and tractors were in greater demand than ever. A plethora of small manufacturers sprang up, as it seemed that anyone who could couple a proprietary engine to a transmission and mount it on four, three or even two wheels could build a tractor. Many of these lesser-known concerns soon disappeared into obscurity, but the British tractor industry was beginning to flourish as many of the big names became established on the market.

Fordson tractors were still rolling out of Dagenham, and David Brown had returned to tractor production at Meltham Mills after diverting the factory's resources to wartime materials. On a much smaller scale, Marshall was still making its single-cylinder diesel tractors in Gainsborough, and in 1946 Morris Motors joined the fray and announced its Nuffield Universal tractor to be built in at Birmingham. The American International Harvester Company also set up tractor production at its British Wheatley Hall plant in Doncaster in 1949.

Harry Ferguson launched his TE-20 tractor from the Standard Motor Company's Banner Lane works in Coventry in 1946. Production began slowly, but Ferguson soon became Britain's largest tractor manufacturer, building over 300 machines a day. The major players were all now in place and it was the beginning of a golden age for the British tractor industry. Agriculture was becoming a highly mechanised industry, the UK was at the forefront of many of the developments and its farm machinery was in demand all over the world.

New Massey Ferguson tractors leave the Banner Lane plant at Coventry in 1999. The factory belongs to the North American conglomerate, AGCO, and is one of only four major tractor plants that were still operating in the UK at the turn of the millennium.

British tractors became recognised in all four-corners of the globe and were operating from Alaska to Australia and Africa to the Antarctic.

The mid-1960s was a watershed period of tractor design with new, more modern lines of machines introduced for world markets. Banner Lane, now home to Massey Ferguson, and the Doncaster and Meltham Mills plants were still in full flow, but Gainsborough was limited to Track-Marshall crawler production. Ford had moved its tractor lines to a new purpose-built factory at Basildon in Essex, which the company claimed was the most modern and automated tractor plant in Europe. Nuffield production was transferred to Bathgate in Scotland, and the tractors were sold under the Leyland name from 1969.

Britain also had a number of thriving smaller companies, such as the four-wheel drive tractor manufacturers, County, Roadless and Muir-Hill, whose specialist products had won worldwide recognition. Ford became the market leader in 1973, and Basildon had its best ever year in 1977 with an annual production figure of nearly 48,000 tractors.

The 1970s saw British tractor production at its zenith with sales starting to decline by the end of the decade. There was increased competition from abroad with more manufacturers chasing fewer sales as farmers bought less, but larger, tractors with higher specifications. A

recession in world agriculture brought about a series of mergers and a rationalisation of manufacturing facilities that would see the tractor industry change beyond recognition through the 1980s.

Leyland was the first name to disappear after the tractor division was sold to the Nickerson Group who already owned Track-Marshall. Production was moved to Gainsborough in 1981, but the company had run into financial difficulties by 1985 and folded. Crawler production continued for a time under new ownership, but petered out during the mid-1990s. County, Roadless and Muir-Hill also ran into financial trouble and ironically went into liquidation within months of each other in 1983.

The first full-scale merger of the 1980s was the acquisition of International Harvester's farm equipment interests by the giant Texan conglomerate, the Tenneco Corporation, in 1985. Tenneco already owned Case and had bought David Brown's tractor division in 1972. The outcome of the merger was the formation of Case IH. It seemed a

JCB began moved into agricultural tractor production in 1990 and remains the only independent British manufacturer to build tractors in any quantity. The new Fastrac 2150 model, launched in 1999, has a six-cylinder Perkins engine rated at 150 hp.

foregone conclusion that one of the organisation's two British tractor plants would be shut down, and Meltham Mills was closed in 1988.

Britain went into the 1990s with only three of its major tractor plants, Basildon, Banner Lane and Doncaster, still in operation. Few concessions were made to the country's tractor heritage as those famous factories that had been closed were ignominiously razed to the ground one by one to become supermarkets or housing estates. The mergers were by no means over and 1991 saw Ford's worldwide tractor and machinery interests purchased by the Italian Fiat organisation. Ford and Fiat's agricultural and industrial divisions were then amalgamated into a new company operating under the New Holland banner.

During the last year of the twentieth century, New Holland acquired the Case Corporation and began merging their worldwide interests to form a massive global product line. The future of Basildon seems assured as it is one of the keystone plants in the new conglomerate that trades as CNH, but nothing is ever certain in the modern tractor world.

One of the casualties of the merger was the Doncaster plant as the factory and its product lines had to be offered for divestment under European Commission anti-competition guidelines before the deal could be ratified. In December 2000, the Wheatley Hall factory was sold to the Italian tractor manufacturer, Landini SpA, who formed a new UK-based business under the historic name of McCormick Tractors International Ltd. The first McCormick tractors appeared the following January.

Massey Ferguson had been bought by another North American conglomerate, AGCO, back in 1994. Banner Lane remains an important facility within the organisation, but there have been rumours, as yet unsubstantiated, about even its possible closure.

The only remaining independent British manufacturer to build tractors in any quantity is JCB Landpower, a division of the famous JCB construction machinery company based in Staffordshire. JCB makes a range of high-speed tractors sold under the Fastrac name. Changing times have brought changing fortunes for Britain's tractor industry, but at least those plants that remain in operation are still producing several hundred tractors a day for world markets.

McCormick Tractors International represents Britain's latest new tractor line and was the result of the Landini takeover of the Doncaster plant. These McCormick CX90 and MC100 models were the first off the line on 31 January 2001.

Chapter 1: The Dawn of Mechanised Farming

1. During the heyday of steam on the farm, usually regarded as the period from 1890 to the 1930s, the traction engine was extensively used for threshing and cable cultivation. This SH class Ruston & Proctor, an 8 hp engine built in 1912, cost £950 when new. Named 'Tulip Queen', it worked into the 1950s in the hands of a threshing contractor in south Lincolnshire.

Motive Power

2. At the beginning of the twentieth century, the horse still reigned supreme in agriculture and was the most accessible and economical source of motive power available to British farmers. The eventual acceptance of the tractor saw horses in decline by the 1930s, although many farms, particularly in the fenland areas, continued to use them until the 1960s. The photograph shows a three-horse team drawing a Smyth 'Nonpareil' drill.

3. The first tractors appeared crude and expensive and it seemed unlikely that they would ever challenge the dominance of the draught animal. Mr Painter designed his 'Indispensable' tractor for use on his farm at Cholsey in Berkshire. It was built locally by the Wantage Engineering Company in 1905.

Pioneer Tractors

4. A rare photograph of an early Saunderson tractor at work in 1908 near Washington in West Sussex. Introduced in 1905, the three-wheel 'Universal' model from Saunderson & Gifkins was powered by a 30 hp four-cylinder engine, advertised as capable of running on petrol or alcohol.

5. Designed in 1913 by A.K. Smith, this 30 hp machine was built by the Omnitractor Syndicate of Great St. Helens, London. The tractor, which weighed 3 ½ tons, is seen outside the Hemmel Hempstead workshops in 1916. Advertised as suitable for agricultural, haulage or military work, it was powered by a twin-cylinder paraffin engine and had a two-speed transmission. It was priced at £500.

6. The renowned stationary engine manufacturers, Petters Ltd. of Yeovil in Somerset, built a very small number of 'oil traction engines' mainly for export. This 22 hp machine was exhibited at the Royal Show held at Norwich in June 1911 and had a single-cylinder semi-diesel engine cooled by the large cylindrical radiator. The distinctive drive wheels were supplied by Atlas Cast Iron Road Wheels of Manchester. Note the elaborate exhaust silencer.

7. This motor plough was something of a departure for the famous steam engine maker, Robey of Lincoln. It was an unwieldy three-wheel machine, powered by an oil engine, with a four-furrow plough mounted beneath its heavy frame. The two large driving wheels were cleverly arranged so that they both ran in the furrow, one in front of and the other behind the plough. Priced at £138, it was entered in the 1916 Royal Show at Manchester, but failed to make an appearance.

The Ivel Factory

The Ivel, designed and built by Dan Albone of Biggleswade in Bedfordshire, was the first successful British tractor. Named after a local river, it was introduced in 1902 and sold in reasonable numbers both at home and abroad. Albone also manufactured bicycles, motor cars, ball-bearings and wheels. Sadly, he did not live to see his tractor developments through as he died in 1906, aged only forty-six years. His death was believed to have been brought on prematurely by the after effects of being struck by lightning while demonstrating the tractor in a thunderstorm.

8. Dan Albone's Ivel was powered by a two-cylinder horizontally-opposed engine that developed around 24 hp and had a single forward and reverse-speed transmission. Early examples had trembler coil ignition while this 1913 model was fitted with a magneto. The tractor weighed nearly two tons and around 500 were built.

9. Was this the first British tractor factory? The Ivel Works in Shortmead Street, Biggleswade, was little more than a corrugated tin shed adjoining the former Ivel Hotel. Albone, seen on the right of the group, originally established the works in 1880 to build and repair cycles before forming Ivel Agricultural Motors in 1903.

10. An interior view of the Biggleswade works. After Albone's death, the company carried on production until 1921. Several Ivel tractors were exported overseas, and the photograph shows a machine in knocked-down form being crated ready for shipment to Morocco.

MAKER OF

THE IVEL CYCLES,

MOTOR CARS.

PATENT BALL BEARING
CARRIAGE AND MOTOR CAR
WHEELS. CHILD CARRIER.
AND INVENTOR AND MANUFACTURER OF
THE IVEL AGRICULTURAL MOTOR.

11. The tractors were exported to twenty-five different countries. A fully-assembled Ivel destined for Russia is about to be put into its packing case outside the Biggleswade works. The tractor was shipped from London docks to the port of Riga. Note the vulnerable location of the magneto mounted on the front of the chassis frame. The Ivel was priced at £355 ex-works in 1914. The company charged £8 10s extra for the packing crate.

The Baldock Tractor Trials

12. *The first British tractor trials were held at Baldock in Hertfordshire by the Royal Agricultural Society of England in August 1910. Eleven machines were entered but only seven made an appearance, and these consisted of four motor and three steam tractors. The tests conducted included hauling a Harrison McGregor binder in a crop of wheat.*

13. *Two Ivel and two Saunderson motor tractors were entered in the Baldock trials. One of the Ivels is seen hauling a three-furrow plough with which it covered 53 acres in 7 hours and 17 minutes.*

14. *This McLaren, made in Leeds, was one of three steamers demonstrated in the Baldock trials. The other two machines entered were a Mann's steam wagon, also from Leeds, and a steam tractor built by Wallis & Steevens of Basingstoke.*

15. The main site for the trials was an eighty-acre field that was divided into five acre plots for the ploughing tests. The soil in each plot was weighed to measure its consistency so that the comparative performance of the tractors could be determined as fairly as possible. In addition to the ploughing and harvesting competitions, traction tests called on the tractors to haul loaded wagons on the road around a twelve-mile route with long and steep gradients. The machines were also subjected to brake tests to determine the horsepower developed. The judges' report was not published for several months and ruled in favour of the steam engines as the motor tractors had evidently made little impression. The McLaren was awarded a gold medal for first prize, having been judged in the report to have 'best fulfilled the requirements of the trials'.

16. The Ivel tractor was regularly seen at many public demonstrations, many of them staged by Albone himself in the Biggleswade area before his premature death in 1906. Note that this early model has a trembler box in place of the later magneto ignition. The judges at the Baldock trials estimated the cost of ploughing with an Ivel to be under five shillings an acre.

Saunderson Tractors

Herbert Saunderson was one of the leading pioneers of tractor development in Britain. Like Dan Albone, he was based in Bedfordshire and had premises at Elstow. His first machines appeared at the turn of the century and he built up a successful business with a succession of partners, exporting many tractors abroad, before retiring in 1924.

17. A Saunderson Universal Model J tractor at the Royal Show held at Bristol in July 1913. The smallest of Saunderson's 'Universal' range of tractors, the Model J was powered by a two-cylinder vertical engine and rated at 10-12 hp. It would run on petrol or paraffin with the fuel tank mounted in front of the large cooling tank at the rear. Note the forward driving position.

18. This Saunderson Model S was a 45-50 hp machine. Designed for the colonial export market, it weighed over six tons and had a four-cylinder petrol-paraffin engine and a three-speed gearbox. The badge on the side of the fuel tank bears the Saunderson & Mills name that the company traded under until about 1916.

19. During 1916, Saunderson completely redesigned its Universal tractors, giving them a radiator cooling system and a more conventional rear driving position. The model G, rated at 25 hp, had a three-speed gearbox and proved to be an immediate success. The other Saunderson models were eventually dropped from the range while the G, which cost £510 in 1919, remained in production until the mid-1920s.

20. Introduced in 1922, the Saunderson 'Light' tractor was powered by a unique vee-twin engine developing 20 hp. Its modern streamlined appearance belied the fact that it was still an outdated design with a chain drive to the rear wheels. Tractor production ended after Saunderson sold out to Crossley Motors Ltd. of Gorton, Manchester, in 1924.

From Steam to Motor

21. While most traction engine manufacturers were reluctant to give up on steam power, a few companies felt that the coming of the internal combustion engine meant that the writing was on the wall for their products and produced tentative designs for motor tractors. Marshalls of Gainsborough built a small number of paraffin oil tractors from 1906, including this 60 hp four-cylinder model that was entered for trials with the War Office in 1909.

Above: 22. A Marshall Class F Colonial oil tractor working with a Howard six-furrow gang plough in 1911. Designed for overseas markets, the Class F developed around 70 hp and was sold in small numbers to several countries including Canada and Australia.

Below: 23. John Fowler of Leeds remained faithful to the traditional traction engine design for its first oil-engined tractors. This 50 hp machine, seen pulling a steam cultivator, was one of six built in 1912. It was powered by a four-cylinder horizontally-opposed engine running on petrol or paraffin.

Strange Contraptions

With tractor development still in its infancy, the early manufacturers gave free reign to their imagination, often producing many weird and not always wonderful designs. There was no established concept for the agricultural tractor and many different build and wheel configurations were tried out.

24. An ingenious steering mechanism allowed this Ivel tractor to be turned into a self-propelled binder for one-man operation. The cumbersome arrangement was designed by Dan Albone but never really caught on.

25. The motor plough was a design favoured by several manufacturers. It was basically a self-contained power unit with an engine and two driving wheels. Provision was made for various implements to be slung under the rear frame. This American Moline Universal Model D, seen harvesting with a binder, was introduced in 1916 and sold in Britain by John Wallace of Glasgow. It was powered by a two-cylinder-opposed petrol engine developing 18 hp.

26. The Farmer Boy 10-20 was sold in Britain by Morris, Russell & Co. of London. Built from 1916 by the McIntyre Manufacturing Co. of Columbus, Ohio, it was powered by a four-cylinder Waukesha engine. It was a three-wheel machine but had only one single driving wheel.

27. The Fowler Motor Plough was designed by Arthur Wyles who built similar machines under his own name at Manchester. This 1915 model had a two-cylinder petrol engine and weighed 22 cwt when equipped with a two-furrow plough. Note the gear drive to the wheels.

Chapter 2: Impact on Agriculture

28. *The demand for tractors to combat food shortages in Britain during the First World War was met by a number of imported machines from the USA. This International Titan was operated by the Ministry of Munitions and is seen with Land Army girls at Morpeth in Northumberland in about 1918. The Titan 10-20 was a popular machine in the UK and over 3,000 were brought into the country from 1914.*

The First World War

29. The number of tractors working in Britain during the First World War was supplemented by over 5,000 Fordson Model F tractors supplied from the USA under an agreement between Henry Ford and the Ministry of Munitions. The first of the Fordsons arrived at the end of 1917 and were known simply as MOM tractors.

30. The American Waterloo Boy, sold in Britain as the Overtime tractor by the Associated Manufacturers' Company of London, cost £375 in 1917. The forerunner of the John Deere, it was a very well respected machine developing 24 hp from its two-cylinder horizontal engine. The tractor is shown harvesting oats with a McCormick binder.

International Tractors

31. International Harvester's tractors were well-built and reliable machines that quickly gained an enviable reputation in Britain. The 8-16 Junior, launched in Britain in 1919, was a departure for the company with its four-cylinder engine mounted in front of the radiator. This sturdy and practical machine soon proved to be as popular as its larger Mogul and Titan brothers.

32. The 12-25 'twin' Mogul was the largest tractor in the International range to be brought into the UK. Powered by a two-cylinder horizontal engine, it weighed nearly 5 tons and is seen on demonstration in Suffolk. Note the Model T Ford car in attendance.

33. An International 8-16 Junior on belt work, driving a saw bench near Market Rasen in Lincolnshire.

American Tractors

34. The Emerson-Brantingham 12-20 from Rockford in Illinois appeared at the Highland Agricultural Society's tractor trials, held at three centres near Edinburgh, Perth and Glasgow, in October 1917. The tractor, which cost £530, was fitted with a clever chain-hoist mechanism to lift its three-furrow plough out of work. The society's report called it 'a compact and easily worked combination'. Note that the Emerson's front-wheel track was wider than that of the rear wheels.

35. The American Big Bull tractor, powered by a two-cylinder horizontal engine developing 24 hp, was sold in Britain as the Whiting-Bull. It was also entered in the Highland tractor trials as well as the first Lincoln tractor trials organised by the Society of Motor Manufacturers and Traders in September 1919. The tractor was described as 'capable of standing a considerable amount of rough work' and the example in the photograph is seen working at Thornton Farm at Frithville in Lincolnshire in 1918.

36. Powered by a Lycoming four-cylinder petrol engine, the Fageol was built in California for citrus fruit growers. It was an unconventional tractor with tiller steering and strange spiked drive wheels. A rare machine in Britain, it was exhibited at the 1921 Royal Show at Derby. The British agents, G. L. Garrett & Sons Ltd. of Kent, managed to sell a few for work in the local hop fields.

37. The Lauson 12-25 was also offered in Britain for about four years from 1920 by the concessionaires, E. H. Thompson, of Coventry, and was priced at £395. Built in Wisconsin, it was fitted with a Lauson-Midwest four-cylinder engine that would run on petrol or paraffin and had a single-speed transmission. The tractor was awarded a gold medal at the 1920 Lincoln tractor trials.

The Aisthorpe Trials

38. The second Lincoln tractor trials were held at Aisthorpe by the Royal Agricultural Society in 1920. There were thirty-six competitors with both British and American manufacturers represented, as well as tractors from Fiat of Italy and Berna of Switzerland. Steam and cable ploughing outfits were also put through their paces. An American Cleveland-Cletrac 12-20 crawler is seen on the weighbridge. Powered by a Wiedely engine, it had a steering wheel that braked the tracks for turning.

39. Among the twelve different makes of American tractors exhibited at the Aisthorpe trials was this Samson Model M, made in Janesville, Wisconsin, by the General Motors Corporation. It was a compact 12-20 hp machine with a three-speed transmission. It weighed under 30 cwt but cost £275, which was more than double the price of the similar Fordson.

40. J. I. Case of Racine in Wisconsin came away from the trials with a gold medal. The company's 22-40 tractor with its four-cylinder cross-mounted engine was a powerful and well-built machine, but was very expensive at £735.

41. In addition to ploughing classes, the tractors at Ainsthorpe were also subjected to drawbar tests. A British Blackstone crawler, made at Stamford in Lincolnshire, is seen pulling a Fiat 702 and an International Titan. The Blackstone's unique three-cylinder engine atomised its paraffin fuel before injecting it into the combustion chamber for economical running. The tank at the front held compressed air for starting.

Tractors for the 1920s

42. As tractor development progressed, more manufacturers were moving away from the earlier concept of bolting the engine, transmission and other parts to a main steel frame or chassis as it was found that problems with 'frame-whip' could alter the alignment of the components. To combat this, Case introduced a stronger and lighter cast iron frame for its cross-mount models, including this 15-27 tractor that was built from 1919 to 1924.

43. The engine and transmission components of the new International 15-30 'gear-drive' tractor, introduced in 1921, were mounted inside a single-piece cast iron hull for rigidity and strength. The 15-30 (shown) was a popular tractor in Britain, praised for its reliability and smooth running engine with its crankshaft supported by large ball-bearings. It was joined two years later by the similar, but even more successful, 10-20 model.

44. *This rare photograph shows an Austin tractor working with a binder in Lincolnshire. Herbert Austin was the first British manufacturer to adopt unit construction with the engine, gearbox and transmission housings forming the backbone of the machine, a principle pioneered by the Fordson. Launched in 1919, the Austin found it difficult to compete against the cheaper and more reliable Fordson and enjoyed only limited success.*

45. *A Rushton tractor on its first public demonstration, working with a set of disc harrows at the Harper-Adams College Farm in Shropshire in March 1929. The Rushton, built in Walthamstow, was another British copy of the Fordson. However, despite an extensive publicity campaign, sales remained low and the company had run into financial difficulties by 1930.*

Tractors from the 1930s

46. *The depressed state of agriculture in Britain through the 1920s and 1930s did nothing to help stimulate home tractor production. The tractor 'population' in the country remained stagnant at around 30,000 and most of these were of American manufacture, including this 1937 Allis-Chalmers WC seen with a binder in Devon. The WC, introduced in 1934, has the typical tricycle wheel arrangement that was preferred for rowcrop work.*

47. *An Oliver 18-28 pulling a pair of three-furrow Oliver ploughs in tandem at Low Mowthorpe Farm near Kirby Grindalythe in Yorkshire in 1934. The 18-28 was a Hart-Parr design that dated from 1931 and became the Oliver 80 in 1938.*

48. A Marshall 18/30 sold by R. H. Crawford of Frithville ploughing in Lincolnshire in 1935. One of the few British tractors in production, the 18/30 was the replacement for the 15/30 model that was launched in 1930, heralding a new line of single-cylinder diesel tractors from Marshalls of Gainsborough.

49. Autumn and winter ploughing was gradually becoming a job for tractors, and a Canadian Massey-Harris 25/40 with a four-furrow Ransomes Multitrac plough leads an Allis-Chalmers Model U down the furrow near Hereford in September 1935.

Chapter 3: Tractors at War

50. *A Fordson tractor and an International Model 62 combine operated by the Smallfields depot of the Surrey 'War Ag' in 1944. The staff inspect their wage slips during a break in harvesting operations. A team of three normally worked with the combine and took turns to cover meal times to keep the machines continually working.*

The War Ags

As Britain prepared for war over the 1938/39 winter, the Ministry of Agriculture set up County War Agricultural Executive Committees to co-ordinate food production in each district. These bodies, more commonly known as the 'War Ags', operated fleets of tractors and machines that were leased out to farmers.

51. An Allis-Chalmers Model M crawler, belonging to the Cornish War Agricultural Executive Committee, reclaims pastureland for much needed food crops.

52. This American Cleveland Cletrac crawler, the six-cylinder FD model fitted with British Blaw-Knox angledozer equipment, was used by the Surrey War Agricultural Executive Committee for land clearance and is seen working on the Hampton Estates at Seale near Aldershot.

Women at the Wheel

53. 54. *With food production stepped up and the need to bring more acres into production, the British farmer faced severe labour shortages as nearly 50,000 skilled men had been lost from the land to the armed forces during the first two years of the war alone.*
The situation was eased by the mobilisation of the Women's Land Army; a movement set up in 1939 to recruit an auxiliary force of female labour to serve agriculture. Hundreds of the girls trained as tractor drivers, and some were so adept at the job that they were sent out to instruct farmers on the care and use of their machinery.

55. Eager students from the Women's Land Army learn about the intricacies of a Fordson at Boreham House in Essex. This establishment, formerly the Henry Ford Institute of Agricultural Engineering, was used during the war years to train the girls in the use and maintenance of tractors. The Fordson has been sectionalised to show its major components.

56. A Land Army girl demonstrates her ability to handle a Fordson tractor and a three-furrow Oliver plough. Ford built over 140,000 tractors at its Dagenham plant between September 1939 and May 1945.

The Campaign for Food

57. The Fordson at work – the tractor was an indispensable tool in the wartime ploughing campaigns that saw around 61 million extra acres brought into arable production. By 1943, there were 18 million acres of land under the plough in Britain.

58. Two Fordson tractors prepare an autumn seedbed for a new crop of winter wheat. The tractor nearest the camera, drawing a wooden levelling harrow, is fitted with Miller skeleton wheels.

59. *Drilling winter wheat in Essex with a Fordson tractor and a Massey-Harris No. 11 seed drill. Canadian Massey-Harris equipment was imported into the UK through offices in Manchester. The company also had a manufacturing agreement with Blackstones of Stamford.*

60. *A Fordson tractor with an Australian Sunshine Suntyne drill that was distributed in the UK by Dening & Co. of Chard in Somerset. The favourite wartime wheat varieties were Squarehead's Master, Standard Red and Yeoman. Early November was regarded as the optimum drilling time with seed rates of up to 1¾ cwt per acre.*

Wartime Harvest

With wheat production up by over 100 per cent in addition to the barley, oats and rye that were also grown, the harvest months of August and September were an important time and were the culmination of the year's work. Over 80 million tons of crops were harvested in 1943, and mechanisation played an important part.

61. *It's all hands to the deck as Land Army girls tackle a crop of oats with a Fordson tractor and Massey-Harris binder.*

62. *Time was of the essence, and as the corn was harvested and the sheaves were stooked, the tractor and plough goes in to prepare for the following crop.*

63. Harvesting with a binder meant that the sheaves had to be carted, stacked and then threshed at a later date, and the photograph shows a 1939 International W-30 driving a Foster drum near Peterborough. It was a laborious and time-consuming task that was simplified and speeded up by the introduction of the combine harvester.

64. The Allis-Chalmers All-Crop 60 combine was introduced in 1940. The British subsidiary, the Allis-Chalmers Manufacturing Company of Abbeydore in Herefordshire were granted a permit to import a quantity of the combines into the UK for the 1941 harvest, including this example seen working with an International 10-20 tractor.

Opposite: 65. Most of the combines operating in Britain, including this pair of Minneapolis-Moline models working in Berkshire, were American machines brought in under the Lend-Lease agreement. A 1942 Minneapolis-Moline UTS draws a Junior bagger combine while a Fordson follows up with a G4 tanker machine powered by a 'Z' engine. Another Fordson carts the corn.

66. A Case DC tractor draws an International 31T combine near Dereham in Norfolk. The early combines were often referred to as harvester-threshers. The average yield for wheat in Britain during the war was 17 cwt per acre, but up to 33 cwt was recorded on the richer soils.

67. An Oliver Standard 70 harvesting with a Minneapolis-Moline combine in Norfolk. Oliver equipment was distributed in the UK by John Wallace. The streamlined 70 tractor had a six-cylinder engine and was launched in 1938.

Grassland & Livestock Farming

68. Even though much of Britain's pasture was ploughed up to grow arable crops, milk production remained a priority and was increased through improved practices and better grassland management. The tractor became an important tool to the stock farmer and a Fordson is seen using a Cottis sweep to bring hay into the barn.

69. Another Fordson equipped with a hay sweep brings a crop of meadow grass to the stationary baling press.

70. A typical winter scene – a Fordson hitches up to a cartload of manure from the stockyard, ready to take it out to the field where it would be spread by hand.

Lend-Lease

71. *An International W-9 tractor with a four-furrow Fisher Humphries plough. Most of the American tractors used during the Second World War were imported under the Lend-Lease Bill, signed by President Roosevelt on 11 March 1941, allowing Britain to obtain equipment and supplies from the USA with payment deferred until after the war.*

72. *The W-9 was the largest in International's 'W' series of standard tractors. A 1945 example is seen in Warwickshire with a 50-T pick-up baler that has the optional forecarriage attachment to help support the weight of the 14 hp Model U-2 power unit.*

73. Minneapolis Moline equipment was imported under the Lend-Lease agreement by Sale Tilney of Winnersh in Berkshire. This ZTU model on steel wheels is working with a Robot transplanter near St. Albans in Hertfordshire.

74. A Minneapolis Moline GTA tractor with a Canadian Massey-Harris '15' combine operated by the Surrey War Agricultural Executive Committee.

Chapter 4: The Golden Age

75. *This 744PD model was one of the first batch of British Massey-Harris tractors, assembled at Manchester between 1948 and 1949 before production was moved to a new factory at Kilmarnock in Scotland. Seen driving a Bamford Rapid hammer-mill near Dereham in Norfolk, it was powered by a Perkins P6 six-cylinder diesel engine developing 42 bhp.*

76. The postwar period was the beginning of a golden age for British tractors; new makes, new models and new factories appeared as manufacturers expanded and consolidated their product lines in the face of a growing demand for farm mechanisation to feed a starving world. The Newman, built first at Grantham and later at Bristol, was based on the earlier Kendall tractor. The AN4 model is shown with the optional two-cylinder Enfield diesel engine. Like many of the lesser-known British makes that appeared during this period, it struggled to sell and was only on the market for a few years.

77. Allis-Chalmers was one of several American manufacturers to establish a manufacturing base in the UK, assembling a new British Model B tractor at Totton, near Southampton from 1950. This example, seen working in Norfolk, dates from 1952.

Ferguson

78. Harry Ferguson, who had introduced his revolutionary hydraulic draft control system and three-point linkage on the Ferguson-Brown in 1936, opened a new tractor factory at Banner Lane in Coventry in 1946. One of the first of his new models, the TE-20 with a Continental petrol engine, is seen harvesting at Wood Farm, near Ufton in Warwickshire.

79. The little grey 'Fergie' became Britain's best selling tractor and over half-a-million were made. Very many were exported and it was recognised worldwide. A diesel version, the TE-F20, was launched in March 1951.

Nuffield

80. *Morris Motors, part of the Nuffield Organisation, branched out into tractor production with its Nuffield Universal tractor, built in Birmingham from 1946. The DM4 diesel model was fitted with a Perkins P4 engine and is seen driving a New Holland 76 Automaton baler in 1953.*

81. *A pair of Nuffield Universal Four tractors, 1957 and 1958 models with BMC diesel engines, forage harvesting in Lincolnshire. Although it never achieved the same level of sales as Ford or Ferguson, the Nuffield was a well-respected tractor with a loyal following of customers.*

David Brown

82. The Huddersfield-based gear manufacturer, David Brown, launched its first tractor in 1939, but production was affected after the company's output was diverted into war materials. Tractor production resumed in 1945, and the Cropmaster model, introduced two years later, enjoyed a long production run. It was a well-built and reliable machine that established the reputation of the David Brown name.

83. A 1950 David Brown Cropmaster working with a set of disc harrows in north Lincolnshire. The tractor was well specified, and was available with hydraulic lift, a six-speed gearbox and a two-speed power take-off. The vaporising oil model cost £453 in 1951.

84. A David Brown Cropmaster Diesel in action with a set of Bamford D24 mounted disc harrows. The diesel model was introduced in 1949. The CAV battery box for electric starting can just be seen on the right-hand side of the tractor.

85. A 1958 David Brown 25D with a three-ton Pettit cart in south Lincolnshire. The 25D and 30D diesel models appeared in 1953, along with the 25C and 30C vaporising oil tractors. The new range featured a weight transfer system known as the Traction Control Unit or TCU for short.

Internationals at Doncaster

86. The International Harvester Company of Great Britain began tractor production at its Wheatley Hall plant in Doncaster on 13 September 1949. The first machines were based on the American Farmall M model with slight modifications. One of the first British Farmall M tractors is seen leaving the paint booth on the assembly line.

87. Crawler production was introduced at Doncaster in 1953 with the BT-6 and BTD-6 models. The larger BTD-20 crawler with its 135 bhp six-cylinder Rolls Royce diesel engine followed in 1959. This interior shot of the Wheatley Hall plant shows the crawler assembly line in about 1960. Both the 50 bhp BTD-6 models (on the right) and the heavier BTD-20 tractors can be seen under construction.

88. The International B-450 diesel tractor was launched at Wheatley Hall in 1958. This was the regular model; a Farmall version was also available for rowcrop work. Power came from the same 50 bhp BD-264 engine as fitted to the BTD-6 crawler – a low-revving long-stroke unit that had bags of torque but was sometimes difficult to start.

89. The production of International's wheeled tractors was transferred to the nearby Carr Hill plant in 1965, allowing the Wheatley Hall factory to concentrate on crawlers and construction machinery. B-450 tractors are seen on the Carr Hill assembly line in 1967.

Fordson Farming

90. Once the massive wartime production run at the Dagenham plant came to an end, Ford was able to take stock and introduce new models to meet the renewed competition from other manufacturers. The E27N Major of 1945 still had the old side-valve engine, but was fitted with an improved crown-wheel and pinion final drive. It is seen equipped with Roadless DG half-tracks on what looks to be a cold day with the driver's collar turned up against the wind. The plough is a British International B-8A.

91. The replacement for the E27N, the E1A 'new' Major launched in 1951, was a much better tractor with probably the best diesel engine on the market. This example, working on a farm at Dowsby in Lincolnshire, was fitted with a Horndraulic loader with a pallet-tippler attachment for handling potatoes.

92. The Diesel Major was followed by Power Major and Super Major variants in 1958 and 1960 respectively before Ford's 'New Performance' range in a new blue and grey livery was launched in 1963. The 'New Performance' Super Major, seen working with a Roadless Sydelift bale loader, boasted nearly 54 bhp.

Imported Tractors

93. With a growing UK tractor industry, there seemed little need for imported foreign makes, but the European manufacturers were keen to gain a presence in the country and a toe-hold in the thriving British tractor market. The German Hanomag company was represented by H. L. Arnes of London. The KV50 was a useful 55 bhp diesel crawler; it cost £1,875 in 1951, and a few found their way on to British farms.

94. The Continental range of crawlers was made in France by Richard Frères of Lyon using British Perkins diesel engines. Introduced to the UK in 1950, they were marketed by Continental Tractor (Great Britain) Ltd. of Feltham in Middlesex. The CP36 model was powered by a 36 bhp Perkins P4(TA) and cost £1,850 in 1953.

95. A stranger to British shores, this French Sift TL4 tractor was exhibited at the 1952 Royal Show, held at Newton Abbot. Built by the Société d'Installation de Force et de Traction, it was powered by a four-cylinder diesel engine rated at 60 hp. It is doubtful whether any were sold in Britain.

96. Dr. Ferdinand Porsche, the father of the Volkswagen Beetle and a name more usually associated with exotic sports cars, became involved with Allgaier tractors in 1949. The German company adopted the use of air-cooled diesel engines, and the tractors were sold under the Porsche name from 1955. The make was launched in the UK in 1962 by Eurotrac (imports) Ltd. of Dover, but made little impact on the market. Two single-cylinder Junior V models are seen outside a dealership in south Lincolnshire.

Four-Wheel Drive

97. As farmers demanded more from their machines, increasing interest was shown in four-wheel drive as a method of improving the traction and performance of the farm tractor. This American skid-steer machine was evaluated in Britain by the National Institute of Agricultural Engineering. Built in 1949 by the Detroit Tractor Company of Michigan, it was designated the 44-16-B and was powered by a Continental N62 petrol engine. All four wheels were chain driven off a centre axle that incorporated internal-expanding brake shoes for steering.

98. Several British companies were at the forefront of four-wheel drive developments with a number of different drive systems and conversions based on Fordson Major tractors. County Commercial Cars Ltd. of Fleet in Hampshire also used a skid-steer arrangement before pioneering a unique twin propeller-shaft drive system as used on this 1960 prototype machine. The tractor was put into production in August 1961 as the County Super-4.

99. The Land-Rover has been recognised as the archetypal four-wheel drive farm vehicle since its introduction in 1948. What is not so well known is this prototype tractor that the company built on one of its Series 1 chassis. Few details exist, but it appears to have standard Land-Rover running gear with reduction boxes fitted to the axles to compensate for the larger diameter tyres. No serious attempt was made to put it into production.

100. Designed by Berkshire farmer, Pat Saunders, the Paramount Dual Tractor Kit was an attempt to link any two popular makes of tractor together to provide a four-wheel drive machine. The kit consisted of a sub-frame that supported the rear tractor, in this case a Fordson Super Major. The rear unit was connected to the leading tractor, a Ford 3000, via the pick-up hitch. Unfortunately, it was not a great success as it was not unknown for the two tractors to part company if the pick-up hitch became worn.

Chapter 5: Tractors on the Farm

101. By the 1960s, the increased use of tractor power meant that more work could be done in less time – two Fordson Major tractors prepare land for sugar beet while the 1960 Power Major, nearest the camera, drills the crop with a Bean seeder in Lincolnshire.

Sowing

102. Before precision seeders and processed or monogerm seed became available, cup-feed drills, such as this Garrett behind a Fordson Major, were used to sow natural sugar beet at rates of up to 20 lb per acre. The crop then had to be gapped and singled by hand.

103. A David Brown 950 sowing wheat with a Bamford Octopus S30 drill. The S30 had twin seed hoppers feeding a revolutionary propeller seed mechanism and was capable of covering three acres per hour. The 950 tractor was brought out in 1958 to replace the older 30D model.

Spreading & Spraying

104. *The postwar advances in mechanisation were matched by the progressive use of chemicals and artificial fertilisers. A Fordson Major uses an International reciprocating-plate distributor to spread compound fertiliser in south Lincolnshire.*

105. *Many farmers preferred to stay with organic manures, and this International Farmall M operated by Fisons Pest Control of Cambridge uses an Atkinson spreader to broadcast 'skin meal' – a slaughterhouse by-product, prized for its slow release of nutrients into the soil – before brussel sprouts are planted on land in Norfolk.*

106. Improvements in the application and placement of fertilisers saw granular products largely replace powder fertiliser. Another alternative was liquid nitrogen that was injected into the soil. A Fordson Major equipped for the job feeds a crop of greens in Lincolnshire.

107. A Massey Ferguson 35 tractor applies a spring herbicide to a crop of wheat with a Vigzol Yeoman sprayer made by Fisons Pest Control. The 35 tractor replaced the Ferguson TE-20 in 1956 and had a six-speed gearbox and an improved hydraulic system.

Harvesting with Binders

Combines were expensive and only slowly gained acceptance because of some doubt as to their capability to cope with UK conditions and damp crops. There were just 3,000 in use in Britain in 1945 and the binder remained the preferred harvest tool on many farms until well into the 1960s.

108. Harvesting wheat with a binder behind a David Brown 25D tractor. Most of the later tractor binders were driven by the power take-off rather than the land wheel.

109. A 1948 Fordson E27N Major with a Massey Harris binder. The tractor has been fitted with a Perkins P6 diesel engine.

110. *The disadvantage of the binder was that the sheaves had to be threshed at a later date. As an alternative to the threshing machine, a Claas Super combine is used for stationary threshing and is fed sheaves from the stack. A 1957 Fordson Major drives the combine while David Brown and Ferguson tractors haul the trailers.*

Threshing with Tractors

111. A Fordson E27N Major drives a Foster drum at Yaxley near Peterborough in September 1951. By the end of the Second World War, tractors had almost totally taken over from steam as the main source of power for the threshing machine. Note the chaff blower and straw elevator at the rear of the drum.

112. This 1943 International W-30 tractor was still used for threshing duties on a south Lincolnshire farm until well into the 1960s.

Opposite: *113. This Fordson E27N Major fitted with a Perkins P6 diesel would have plenty of power to drive this Marshall drum working near Newark, Nottinghamshire, in August 1953.*

Harvesting with Allis-Chalmers

114. An Allis-Chalmers Model U tractor making hay with a Roto-Baler in Devon. Allis-Chalmers equipment, billed as 'the original orange line', had a loyal following in Britain, and the company's harvesting equipment was widely used.

115. Allis-Chalmers' Roto-Baler was the forerunner of the modern round baler. The pick-up fed a rubber conveyor-belt that rolled the crop into a 3ft long bale. The machine is seen in action with a 1941 Allis-Chalmers WF tractor.

116. This 1951 Model B was one of the first Allis-Chalmers tractors to be made in Britain. In February 1950, the company opened a new factory to build engines and harvesting equipment at Essendine near Stamford. A British version of the All-Crop 60 combine was put into production with a target of 500 planned for the 1951 harvest.

117. A 1954 Allis-Chalmers Model B, fitted with an optional Perkins P3 diesel engine, harvesting with an All-Crop 60 combine. The British production of Model B tractors was eventually moved from Totton to Essendine where they were built at a rate of about 100 per week.

Harvesting with Combines

118. *Self-propelled combines, bulk grain handling, grain silos and drying plants speeded up harvests and cut down on labour. The tractor, such as this Fordson E27N Major seen here with a Massey-Harris 21 combine, completed the harvest operation by carting the grain to the store.*

119. *A Fordson E27N drives a German Claas Super combine while a John Deere carts the corn at Woodhurst in Cambridgeshire in September 1953. The corn sacks would weigh 18 stone.*

120. A Fordson Diesel Major working with a Massey-Harris 750 combine in south Lincolnshire. The tractor-drawn trailed combine was a more economical choice for the smaller farms.

121. A Fordson Dexta with a Ransomes MST42 combine. Built in Ipswich, the Ransomes was based on a Swedish Bolinder Munktell machine.

Potato Growing

122. *Potatoes were a very labour intensive crop to grow until tractors and machinery simplified the planting and harvesting operations. A 1946 Caterpillar D4 in the hands of a Lincolnshire contractor sets potatoes with a Robot planter.*

123. *A John Deere Model B tractor lifts early potatoes with an elevator-digger of the same make. The average yield was around 7 tons per acre, but gang labour was still needed to pick the crop into baskets.*

124. *The late-1950s saw the advent of fully mechanised potato harvesting systems such as this Whitsed Model RB harvester made by Root Harvesters of Peterborough. Introduced in 1957, the RB replaced the earlier 'Z' model and was capable of lifting three acres of potatoes per day. A Fordson Major pulls the harvester while a Dexta catches the crop with a 3-ton Pettit trailer.*

125. *Mechanised potato harvesting the Massey Ferguson way in 1962 – two 35 tractors, a 711 harvester and a 717 trailer. The company claimed its 711 harvester, introduced in 1959, gave potatoes the 'velvet glove' treatment.*

Sugar Beet

126. A 1945 John Deere Model BN hoeing sugar beet. John Deere tractors were extensively used in Lincolnshire and the Fens – their rowcrop design was ideally suited to the type of farming of the area where they were known locally as 'John Pops' because of the distinctive exhaust note of their two-cylinder engines.

127. A 1950 International Farmall M catches the crop while a Nuffield Universal powers the beet harvester near Warboys in Cambridgeshire. Since its introduction to the UK in the early years of the twentieth century, sugar beet has been a crop that has been well suited to mechanisation and there were several types of beet harvesters on the market by the 1950s.

128. This Catchpole Cadet, seen behind a 1952 Fordson Major on a farm at Dowsby in Lincolnshire, was typical of the trailed harvesters of the 1950s. A 1949 Fordson E27N draws the trailer.

129. A 1953 International Farmall BMD delivers a load of sugar beet into Ely factory. Non-tipping trailers had to be washed off by water guns or unloaded by hand. The Farmall BMD, built at Doncaster, was introduced in April 1953 and powered by the BD-264 diesel engine.

Farm Transport

130. *For hauling the crops and general transport around the farm, the horse and cart were largely replaced by the tractor and trailer. There were exceptions, such as this Muir-Hill 'Powacart', a converted wartime dumper based on a Fordson tractor, pressed into service hauling sugar beet on a Lincolnshire farm.*

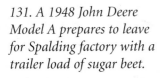

131. A 1948 John Deere Model A prepares to leave for Spalding factory with a trailer load of sugar beet.

132. A 1956 Nuffield Universal carting hay bales. The four-wheel wagon or trolley with its harvest raves was a popular design. This was the Wheatley 'Deeping' model made in Peterborough. It cost £165 complete with sides and could carry up to 7 tons.

133. The standard farm trailer remained the 3-tonner, but to meet the increasing demand for larger capacity trailers, F. W. Pettit of Moulton in Lincolnshire introduced this 7-ton tandem-axle tipper in 1961. The tractor is a Massey Ferguson 65.

Green Crops

134. A Fordson Dexta cutting peas for vining in south Lincolnshire. The design of the rear-mounted swather meant that the tractor had to be driven in reverse.

135. Two Fordson E27N Majors, both fitted with Perkins diesel engines, working with a Hume green-crop loader loading windrowed peas near Benwick, Cambridgeshire, in August 1951. The peas, which were grown for canning, would then be transported to a static viner.

136. *Picking dwarf French beans with a Mather & Platt harvester in 1962. The power unit is an International B-275 High-Clear tractor that was built at International Harvester's satellite plant at Idle near Bradford in Yorkshire.*

137. *The work involved in large scale vegetable growing was simplified by mechanical transplanters such as this Russell Multiplanter on a Leverton toolbar, seen planting seedlings behind a David Brown 30D in south Lincolnshire – one of the most intensive green-growing areas in the country.*

Grassland Farming

138. *Making hay while the sun shines with a Fordson Major and a Bamlett self-lift tractor mower.*

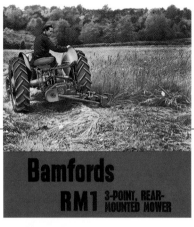

Bamfords
RM1 3-POINT, REAR-
MOUNTED MOWER

139. *With grassland at a premium in the arable fenlands, it was common practice for those farmers who kept stock to mow and bale the roadside verges for hay. A three-wheel Nuffield Universal M3 is seen with an Allis-Chalmers Roto-Baler in 1960.*

140. Linconshire farmers, Burtts of Dowsby, grew grass for seed. This 1947 Fordson E27N Major is swathing creeping red fescue for fine lawn or golf course seed.

141. When dry, the grass for seed was collected and moved to the threshing drum or clover huller by this ex-Royal Air Force Queen Mary transporter pulled by a Fordson E27N Major.

Forage Harvesting

142. *An Oliver 80 and an American Fox forage harvester on trial with the National Institute of Agricultural Engineering. The principle of ensilage as a method of storing grass for fodder became more widespread during the Second World War. The process was made easier by the onset of mechanisation and the tractor-drawn foragers that both chopped and collected the crop. The Fox forage harvester, built in Wisconsin by the Fox River Tractor Company, was imported by Sale Tilney from 1945.*

143. *This Johnson forage harvester, made in March, Cambridgeshire, was based on the American Fox machine but was fitted with an auxiliary Perkins diesel engine. It is seen in October 1952 being drawn by a wartime Fordson while an E27N collects the crop.*

144. A Fordson Major cutting lucerne in Warwickshire in June 1960. The forage harvester is a New Holland model 800, introduced in 1959 and fitted with a six-cylinder Continental auxiliary engine. Capable of an output of 45 tons per hour, the 800 cost £1,946.

145. A 1960 Fordson Dexta in a crop of lucerne with a Sila-Masta forage harvester made by John Wilder of Wallingford in Berkshire. Introduced in 1959, the Sila-Masta was based on the Wilder-Rainthorpe straw chopper.

Silage & Manure

146. *A rather dilapidated E27N Major consolidates a silage clamp in Sussex. 'Where there's muck there's brass' is an old adage that will be refuted by most livestock and dairy farmers; their tractors were never as immaculate as those found in the arable eastern counties of England, and were often corroded by the ravages of manure and fermenting silage.*

147. *This Fordson E27N was used to carry the grass from the field with its buckrake and then consolidated the clamp with its open cage wheels to ensure there were no air pockets to turn the crop mouldy.*

148. A Nuffield Universal M3 three-wheeler shifts manure with a Horndraulic rear-loader. An unenviable task that was guaranteed to give the driver neck ache.

149. A Fordson Super Dexta with a Roadless four-wheel drive conversion is down to its axles in chicken manure as it loads a muckspreader in Surrey in 1960.

Chapter 6: Tractors in Industry

150. Many agricultural tractors were adapted for industrial use. The Fowler 'Patent' oil tractor seemed equally at home on the road or in the field. It is seen hauling two wagon-loads of bricks in Yorkshire in 1912.

Road Haulage

151. A rare photograph of an Ivel tractor being used for road haulage with a local removals firm in Biggleswade in about 1904. The pantechnicon would normally have been pulled by horses; the tractor would be no faster and was probably more expensive to run.

152. A Barford & Perkins tractor uses a 12-ton Garrett trailer to haul brick rubble near Peterborough in 1930. Designed for both agricultural and industrial use, this 1927 prototype machine was based on the company's THD road roller. It had Roadless tracks and was powered by a supercharged two-cylinder McLaren-Benz diesel developing 50 hp. Its weight of 11 tons deterred any potential customers and only the one was built.

Industrial Tractors

153. Industrial versions of agricultural tractors were an effective source of motive power in the 1930s. They were faster than horse-drawn vehicles and more economical than steam wagons. International Harvester was among the first companies to offer industrial models. This 10-20, with improved braking, solid rubber tyres, a sprung front axle, a lighting set and an enclosed cab, was used in London by the John Mowlem construction company.

154. Early British manufacturers of industrial tractors included Austin and Rushton. Austin production was transferred to Liancourt, near Paris, during the early-1920s and an improved model with a slightly more powerful engine was introduced. The industrial version is seen at the tractor's re-launch on the British market in 1931. A diesel model followed two years later.

155. *This experimental industrial tractor, seen at the Public Works Exhibition, was built in 1931 by John Fowler of Leeds. It was powered by a four-cylinder petrol engine. Only two were made, and both were sold for municipal work in Scotland while the company turned its attentions to crawler production.*

156. *Marshalls of Gainsborough introduced its single-cylinder line of two-stroke diesel tractors at the World Tractor Trials in 1930. This Model E 15/30 industrial dates from 1932 and has a sprung front axle, down-swept exhaust, lighting and a horn. A similar machine was used by the company for general haulage in their own factory.*

Winch Tractors

157. *Auto-Mower Engineering from Somerset built a number of winch tractors and truck conversions from 1929. This Auto-Tractor winch truck, based on Ford components, appeared in 1934. Designed for timber extraction, it was fitted with a V8 petrol engine.*

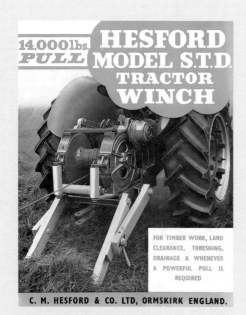

158. *Most Auto-Mower winch conversions were based on Fordson tractors, and this adaptation of an Allis-Chalmers Model U would be a rare machine. An extended frame at the front of the machine provided mounting points for the winch and ground anchor. The long guard shielded the chain drive to the winch. The rear wheels were fitted with Opperman strakes for extra traction.*

Industrial Tugs

159. This 1947 Clark tug was used on a Fenland farm for road haulage, including moving the Caterpillar D2 crawler from field to field with the low-loader. The little industrial tug was made at Battle Creek, near Michigan in the USA and would have been more at home in a factory or towing aircraft. Known as the Clarktor-6, it was powered by a six-cylinder petrol engine.

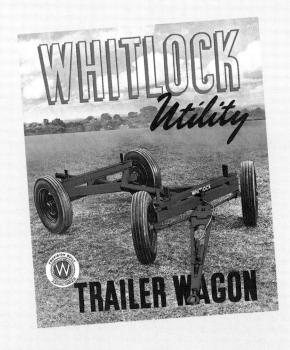

160. This industrial tug conversion was based on a Morris car. Fitted with a three-cylinder Perkins P3(V) diesel engine, it is seen working in a timber yard at Kings Lynn in March 1959.

Ford in Industry

161. *Few other manufacturers had as great an impact on the industrial tractor market as the Ford Motor Company. The first postwar industrial Fordson tractor, based on the E27N Major, appeared in 1947. It had a petrol engine, larger drum brakes, electric lighting and starting, an enclosed steel cabin with a canvas canopy, and an automatic towing hitch fixed to a channel-iron frame, all for £395.*

162. *An agricultural Fordson E27N Major, fitted with a Perkins diesel, provides the power for a stone crusher at Border Quarries near Galashiels in Scotland.*

163. Fordsons go where other tractors fear to tread – an E27N, equipped with Rotaped tracks and a Muledozer attachment, is lowered into London's sewers to clean sludge out of the drains.

164. Much of the municipal work was unglamorous (and often smelly) as shown by this photograph of a Fordson Diesel Major working on a council tip near Enfield in Middlesex. The tractor was fitted with steel front wheels and Rotaped tracks to avoid tyre damage by broken glass. It has a later hydraulic Muledozer and a Winsam cab.

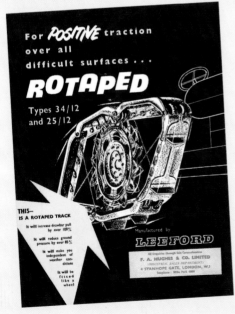

For *POSITIVE* traction over all difficult surfaces . . .

ROTAPED

Types 34/12 and 25/12

THIS—
IS A ROTAPED TRACK

It will increase drawbar pull by over 100%

It will reduce ground pressure by over 85%

It will make you independent of weather conditions

It will be fitted like a wheel

Manufactured by

LEEFORD

All Enquiries through Sole Concessionaires

F. A. HUGHES & CO. LIMITED
(INDUSTRIAL SALES DEPARTMENT)
4 STANHOPE GATE, LONDON, W.1
Telephone: MAYfair 6000

Chapter 7: Sales & Service

165. *With no established dealers to sell the early tractors, sales were handled by the manufacturers, importers or concessionaires, with motor garages or blacksmiths appointed as local agents. The American Big Bull tractor was sold in Britain from 1919 as the Whiting-Bull by the London store, Whiting Ltd. of Euston Road.*

The Early Agencies

166. An Emerson Model L tractor on demonstration in 1916. Brainsby's Ltd. of Broadway, Peterborough, held the British agency for the American Emerson-Brantingham tractors until the concession was taken over by Melchior, Armstrong & Dessau of London in the early 1920s.

167. A Herefordshire dealer for Overtime tractors publicises its local demonstration by parading the machines through the middle of Leominster. There was much resistance among many farmers to the tractor – they believed it was an unnecessary and expensive tool that would damage the land, and felt that a volatile spirit such as petrol had no place on the farm. A well-organised demonstration was the agent's best chance of persuading them otherwise.

The First Dealerships

168. The Ford Motor Company, having had a presence in Britain since 1911, could draw on its network of motor car dealers to act as agents for the Fordson tractor. A stand belonging to the Willenhall dealer, Reginald Tildesley, is seen at the 1924 Staffordshire Agricultural Show. The agricultural Model F Fordson is priced at £128, while the industrial model on the left is £191. The Model T truck in the middle cost £140.

169. Mogul 8-16 tractors lined up outside an early International Harvester dealership in Dorset. The premises belonged to T. Dibben & Sons, Motor Engineers of Wimborne. The Mogul 8-16, built from 1914 to 1917, was the first International tractor to be imported into Britain and cost £320.

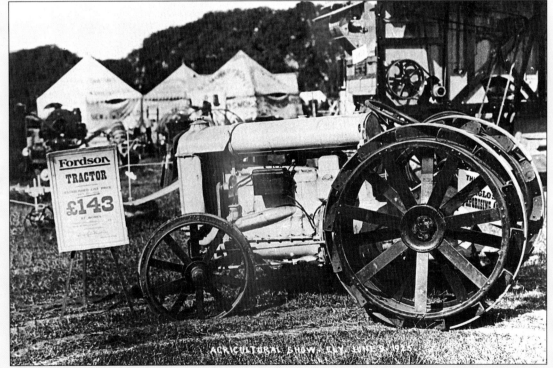

170. A Model F Fordson on a local dealer's stand at an agricultural show held at Ely in Cambridgeshire in June 1925. Note that the price of the tractor is now £143. The box on the side of the engine housed the trembler coils for the ignition system.

Robert H. Crawford

171. Bob Crawford established this blacksmith's shop at Frithville, near Boston in Lincolnshire, in 1920. He built implements and took on the agencies for several makes of machinery, selling his first tractor, the International 10-20 seen on the left of the photograph, in 1922.

172. Before long, R. H. Crawford was a respected implement maker with a thriving business selling new and second-hand machinery. The company is seen exhibiting at the 1933 Lincolnshire Show where it was awarded the Challenge Cup for its stand. The variety of machines on display include two Marshall 18/30 tractors and a number of implements of Crawford's own manufacture.

173. A pair of horses brings an International 10-20 tractor into Crawford's workshop for repair in 1925. Bob Crawford both built and mended machinery and had one of the first oxyacetylene welders in the district.

174. A local farmer collects a Clayton & Shuttleworth crawler from Crawford's Frithville premises in 1935. R. H. Crawford held the franchises for Austin, Caterpillar and Oliver tractors, as well as many leading makes of oil engines, ploughs, cultivators, barn and harvesting machinery. The company was also appointed main agents for Marshall-Fowler equipment.

175. R. H. Crawford's trade card of 1947. Today the firm is a flourishing and well-known machinery dealership and is run by Bob's son, Robert, who has been recently joined by his son, also Robert and the third generation of the family to enter the business.

Agricultural Engineers

176. By the 1940s, tractors were sold and serviced by agricultural engineers who were usually agents for a variety of machines. These firms were often implement makers who also undertook blacksmith and general repair work. A McCormick binder, two Fordson tractors, an International W-6 and a Ransomes cultivator are lined up outside Fenton & Townsend's North Road Works in Sleaford, Lincolnshire.

177. Ernest Doe & Sons evolved from a humble blacksmith's shop to become one of the largest tractor dealers in the south-east of England. By 1941, the company held the agencies for at least seven different makes of tractor, and a new Fordson and a Case LA (on the right) are seen in the yard at Ulting. The veteran machines in the background are trade-ins that were stripped for spares and then scrapped for the war effort.

178. A Massey-Harris 21 combine, a Minneapolis-Moline G8 combine, A John Deere B tractor and a Fowler FD3 crawler illustrate the range of machines sold by P. B. Bettinson of Holbeach, Lincolnshire in the late-1940s. The company later moved away from sales into manufacturing and became better known for its cage wheels and seed drills.

Promoting the Tractor

With so many new models on the market after the Second World War, dealers had to learn new methods of promoting their products to stay ahead of the competition. The Devon Allis-Chalmers distributor, John L. C. Flew, took sales promotion seriously and initiated an unprecedented advertising campaign during the late-1940s that was accompanied by some unique photographs.

179. Allis-Chalmers' advertising slogan for the Model B tractor was 'A Symbol of Better Living'. Taking this one stage further, Flew even suggested that you would want to go fishing on your tractor in your spare time!

180. The manufacturer's sales leaflets were a cost effective method of promoting the tractor.

181. Glamour as an advertising tool is a relatively modern concept, but not one that is often connected with farm machinery. Using a scantily clad female to promote this Allis-Chalmers Model C tractor would have been regarded as risqué in the 1940s.

182. John L. C. Flew's stand at an agricultural show in the late-1940s. Three Model B tractors, an All-Crop 60 combine, a Roto-Baler and other items of Allis-Chalmers equipment are on display. The company was a respected family firm with a reputation for good service.

Lincolnshire Dealers

183. C. C. Nichols of Gainsborough was the local distributor for Marshall and Fowler equipment. The company's Jowett Bradford service vans are seen outside its premises with new Series 2 Field Marshall tractors and a Fowler FD3 crawler in 1947.

184. Frank Crawford of Moulton Chapel was typical of the smaller machinery dealers of the 1950s, holding several agencies and supplying most of the needs of the local farming community. Allis Chalmers tractors, a Melotte plough and GBW beet-harvesting equipment can be seen on the forecourt, that also served as the village filling station.

185. International B-450 Farmall tractors lined up outside Johnson Brothers' showrooms in Spalding in 1962. In addition to holding a main dealership for International Harvester equipment, the business, which dated back to 1907, also operated as heating and electrical engineers, ironmongers and builders' merchants.

186. A deal for twenty new MF 35 tractors for one local farm is concluded at the Kirton premises of the Massey Ferguson dealership, Boston Tractors, in 1960. The company had been Ferguson dealers since 1947 and had branches in Kirton and Holbeach. Part of the Kirton showroom was converted from a chapel.

Levertons of Spalding

187. With south Lincolnshire being such a intensely arable area, it had more than its fair share of tractor dealers, but none were as well known as Levertons of Spalding. This 1959 works photograph confirms the diversity of the operation with both Nuffield and Caterpillar equipment in the yard. Leverton pea-cutters can be seen on the right.

188. On-farm service was a facility offered by most postwar dealerships. Levertons' Austin A40 Devon was typical of the dealers' service vans of the 1950s, fitted with 'Town & Country' tyres at the rear for off-road use.

189. Owned by the Myers family, H. Leverton Ltd. dated back to 1904, becoming important Caterpillar, John Deere, Nuffield and Lanz main dealers, as well as machinery manufacturers in their own right. The workshops were always busy, and the photograph shows both Caterpillar and Nuffield tractors under repair. Nearest the camera is a 'J' model D2.

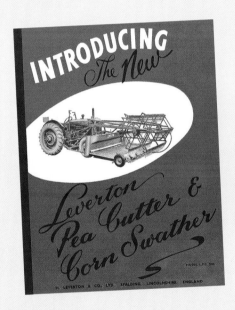

190. Levertons' Caterpillar sales and service territory extended to nearly half of the UK, and the Spalding depot offered a full reconditioning and overhaul service.

Workshop & Stores

191. R. H. Crawford's workshops at Frithville in the 1950s. Ford, Lister and Fowler Gyrotiller engines are under repair while a hydraulic lift for a Fordson E27N lies nearest the camera. Fowler Challenger, Oliver and Ferguson tractors can be seen in the back of the workshop.

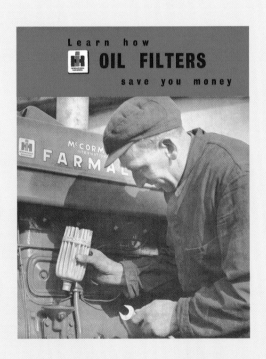

192. The track running-gear on a BTD-6 crawler receives an overhaul at an International Harvester dealership. A bar is used to adjust the tension of the track spring and front idler assembly.

193. The workshops of main dealers would be kept busy repairing both tractors and machinery. A Fordson Diesel Major gets a thorough overhaul at a Ford dealership. A fitter has the engine stripped out on the workbench while his mate checks the clutch thrust-bearing.

194. The stores in a dealership were a fascinating place in the 1950s, well stocked with tractor and implement spares, belts, hoses, lubricants, baler twine, nuts, bolts, nails and just about everything the farmer would need to keep his machines moving. An experienced storeman had a good knowledge of the parts, knew exactly where they were stored in the bins or racks, and could usually quote part numbers off the top of his head.

On-Farm Repairs

195. The alternative to main dealer service was the farm workshop and many of the larger farms had their own mechanics. This 3,000-acre farm in Lincolnshire could justify two full-time fitters, seen changing the battery on this Cleveland Cletrac 40 crawler during the 1950s. The tractor was built in 1936 and had a six-cylinder Hercules diesel engine.

196. Another option for getting the repairs done was the local blacksmith. If parts were no longer available or too expensive, he could usually fabricate what was needed. By the 1950s, the blacksmith was more likely to be found working on tractor implements than shoeing horses.

197. Not all farms were well equipped for breakdowns, but a handful of tools and a little mechanical knowledge could often save money on maintenance. A wheel bearing adjustment on a Fordson E27N was one of the simpler tasks that could be carried out in the workshop.

198. A typical on-farm repair – if in doubt, hit it with a hammer! A home-made trolley, a wooden track and a front-end loader help make easy work of splitting a Fordson.

The Agricultural Show

The agricultural show was an important event on the social and business calendar. It gave the dealers the opportunity to exhibit their products in the marketplace and meet both old and new customers.

199. The Turner 'Yeoman of England' tractor on the company's stand at the Royal Show held at Shrewsbury in 1949. Built in Wolverhampton, the Turner had a vee-four diesel engine and just over 2,000 were built before production ended in 1955.

200. The finishing touches are made to Marshall's stand at the 1953 Royal Show at Blackpool. A Fowler Challenger 1 crawler, powered by a Marshall two-cylinder two-stroke ED5 diesel engine, receives a final lick of paint prior to the show opening.

201. Boston May Fair gave R. H. Crawford the opportunity to exhibit its wares in the middle of the town centre. This line-up in 1946 includes a Massey-Harris combine, a British Anzani Iron Horse, Fordson and Field Marshall tractors.

202. A variety of machinery, including Caterpillar and Nuffield tractors, Lanz and Leverton equipment on H. Leverton's stand at the Peterborough Show in the 1950s.

203. *Frank Crawford's stand at the 1958 Peterborough Show offered a diversity of equipment, including Fordson, Massey Ferguson and County tractors in addition to Allis-Chalmers, Atkinson, Gascoigne, Horndraulic, Lister, GBW, Pettit and Cooks machinery. Unlike today, farming was buoyant, farmers had money in their pocket and several important deals would be concluded before the show ended.*

204. A colourful display from the Ford main dealer, Crimble of Staines, for the 1960 Surrey County Show held in Guildford. The Fordson Super Major on the left of the stand is fitted with a Bomford hedge-cutter attachment while the yellow County CD50 industrial crawler is equipped with a Bray angledozer.

205. Part of the machinery line at the 1963 Royal Show at Stoneleigh in Warwickshire with stands from notable British manufacturers such as Cooks, County Tractors, Midland Industries, Roadless Traction and McConnell. County's display includes (left to right) a swamp crawler, a four-wheel drive Super-6, a Super Dexta timber tractor and a Super-4 model.

Demonstrations

206. Tractor demonstrations were a good way to encourage sales and promote new models, giving farmers a chance to see the machines in action. Fenland silt soil allows a 40 bhp B-414 tractor to run away with a four-furrow B1-42 plough at this demonstration of International Harvester equipment held in 1961. The crawler in the background was the new BTD-8 model, launched in 1960 with the more powerful 58 hp BD-281 engine.

207. *Roadless's demonstration tractor draws an interested crowd of spectators as it is put through its paces in 1959. The four-wheel drive machine was based on the Fordson Power Major using a GMC ex-military truck axle driven by a sandwich transfer box. Roadless Traction of Hounslow in Middlesex built a succession of tracked vehicles before turning to four-wheel drive in 1956 with a conversion made under licence from Selene of Italy.*

208. *A John Deere 4020 on demonstration in Essex in August 1963. After an absence of several years from the British market, John Deere re-established a UK base, taking over Lundell of Edenbridge in Kent in 1961. Built at the American Waterloo plant, the six-cylinder 4020 cost £1,875 and became one of the company's best-selling tractors of all time.*

Chapter 8: Men & Machines

209. A welcome break from ridging potatoes with a Ferguson TE-F20 diesel during the 1950s. What is a good tractor driver? According to a Rushton booklet of 1929, 'He is one who can keep his tractor and implements in first-class condition, do satisfactory work on the land, avoid breakdowns and do his own minor repairs.'

210. Even by the 1950s, many of the tractor drivers had served their farming apprenticeships with horses. When tractors first appeared, mechanics from the local garage or neighbouring town were trained as drivers; they could operate machinery but knew little of the rudiments of farm work. The farmers soon realised that it was better to train experienced farmhands, who already knew all about ploughing and harvesting techniques, how to handle a tractor.

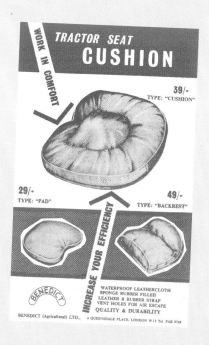

211. The skill and tenacity of the tractor drivers was often overlooked; these were the men who worked in all weathers with little protection other than an ex-army greatcoat to keep out the cold and a hessian sack to sit on. A good man could coax a temperamental and unwilling engine while still managing to plough, drill or draw out potato rows as straight as a die.

Weather Cabs

The weather cab made an appearance once farmers realised the importance of keeping the tractors working in all weathers. The early cabs remained crude, usually made from wood or canvas, until improved sheet-metal designs were brought out in the 1950s.

212. The wood and corrugated iron structure fitted to this International 12-25 Mogul makes it look like a chicken shed on wheels.

213. Roadless offered this canvas canopy as an optional extra for its tracked version of the Case Model C crawler in 1935. The canopy was made for the company by Stanhay of Ashford in Kent.

214. A 1951 Hanomag K55 crawler fitted with a Sun-Trac steel cab.

215. *This Sun-Trac cab looks too modern for this Oliver 90 tractor. Made by Tractor Supplies of Wolverhampton, a company started by an ex-Levertons employee, Frank Wootton, the extensive Sun-Trac range included a cab to fit most British, American and European tractors operating in the UK.*

216. *H. Leverton Ltd. made its own cabs to fit both Caterpillar and John Deere tractors. This cab, seen fitted to a 1944 John Deere Model B, was a typically basic structure. No doors were fitted and the driver had to clamber up over the back to gain access.*

Tractors in the Wet

One of the more interesting aspects of operating tractors in Britain is coping with the vagaries of the weather. The farmer remains at the mercy of the damp British climate and wet seasons have to be expected.

217. Even the tracks are spinning on this Allis-Chalmers Model M crawler as it tries to keep the All-Crop 60 combine moving during a very wet harvest in the 1950s.

218. A wet autumn in 1960 sees two John Deere Model A tractors chained together in an attempt to keep this Catchpole Cadet beet harvester working.

219. Before differential locks were fitted, getting stuck was an unavoidable occurrence in the wet. Several days' rain and a patch of soft ground meant that even the Bower strakes fitted to the rear wheels of this Fordson E27N were not enough to stop it from becoming completely bogged-down.

220. Sometimes tractors were called on to perform tasks in the wet when other vehicles were out of their depth. Two Fordson tractors working with a Sigmund pump help clear up in Essex after hurricane-force winds combined with high tides to swamp England's east-coast flood defences in February 1953.

Wheel Equipment

221. *Several different types steel wheels and methods of increasing traction in the wet were marketed with varying degrees of success. This Allis-Chalmers Model U tractor has been fitted with a pair of steel wheels made by the Unitcast Corporation of Toledo, Ohio, for trials by the National Institute of Agricultural Engineering.*

222. *Strakes were heavy attachments that bolted to the rear wheels to provide extra traction when the going was tough. This 1947 Fordson E27N Major is shown ploughing with Darvill retractable strakes made by Stanhay. The other popular makes were Bower and Opperman. The plough is an International.*

223. Several half-track conversions were available for extreme conditions. The Rotaped track units, seen on this Fordson Power Major, consisted of six jointed pans kept in formation by a tensioned chain arrangement. They were manufactured in Hertfordshire by George Monro until Leeford took over the design in the 1950s.

224. Autumn drilling with a Fordson Super Major fitted with open cage wheels to reduce soil compaction. Similar equipment was marketed by both Humberside Agricultural Products and Catchpole, while quick-fit cage wheels, such as the Molcage wheels made by P. B. Bettinson, appeared in the late-1960s.

Fuel

225. A horse and cart is used to deliver fuel to a Fordson working at Toft Farm near Dunchurch in Warwickshire in 1942. Early tractors either ran on straight petrol or a heavier distillate such as paraffin or kerosene. Paraffin was less refined than petrol and was a cheaper fuel but needed a vaporiser to heat the fuel to convert it into an inflammable vapour. The use of tractor paraffin or vaporising oil came about because the less efficient refining processes of the time meant that the oil companies had large quantities of 'middle distillates' available which were sold cheaply to power farm machinery.

226. A wartime Fordson is refuelled from a 5-gallon can. Tractors running on paraffin or vaporising oil were fitted with a twin-compartment fuel tank to allow them to be started and warmed up on petrol. Note the makeshift heat-shield fitted to the tractor's manifold. Shell was the first company to market branded vaporising oil, which it sold as TVO, standing for Tractor Vaporising Oil. Although TVO was a Shell trademark, the term was eventually adopted into general usage as a generic name for the fuel.

227. Gathering winter fuel: a fuel tanker operated by the Esso Petroleum Company delivers tractor diesel to a farm at Harberton in Devon in 1958. By the 1950s, most tractor manufacturers were moving over to the more efficient and economical compression-ignition engines that ran on diesel fuel. Rebated fuel for use in agriculture contained a dye and was known as 'red diesel' or gas oil.

228. A Doe Triple D is refuelled with BP 'Diesolite' tractor diesel on Lord Rayleigh's Farm's in Essex in 1961. The Triple D was an ingenious venture to build a 100 hp four-wheel drive tractor. Built locally by Ernst Doe & Sons, it was based on two Super Major skid units that articulated in the middle. This meant that the driver had two fuel tanks to fill.

Farm Safety

Farm machinery can be dangerous, but complacency breeds contempt; mechanical failure and human error were often responsible for too many avoidable accidents involving tractors despite vigorous safety campaigns by the Ministry of Agriculture, the Royal Society for the Prevention of Accidents and latterly the Health & Safety Executive.

229. The weather cab on this Nuffield offered the driver no protection after the tractor overturned. A total of 155 people were killed on British farms through overturning accidents between 1952 and 1957.

230. This accident appears to have been caused by a loose trunnion pin that allowed the Fordson Power Major's front axle to come adrift, forcing the tractor off the road. The drainage ditches in the low-lying Fens could be a hazard for the unsuspecting tractor driver if the edges were unstable or loose.

231. *This Nuffield Universal lost its battle with a railway locomotive after a disastrous encounter at an unmanned level crossing in the fog. The old Great Northern Railway sign was a poignant reminder of the dangers involved in crossing a mainline track.*

FARM SAFETY

Tractors Overturning

During the past five years, some 155 people working in agriculture in Great Britain were killed by tractors overturning. Nearly all these accidents were due to human errors and could have been avoided if more care had been taken.

CARE AND COMMON SENSE REDUCE THE DANGER OF OVERTURNING

232. *Levertons' crane is called in to recover an Allis-Chalmers Model M crawler from the ditch while a Caterpillar D2 stands by to assist. The Hyster crane, built in 1949, looks easily capable of handling the three-ton weight of the crawler.*

Tractor Ploughing

233. Trailed ploughs, such as this three-furrow Ransomes Midtrac, remained the norm until mounted ploughs gained in popularity during the late-1940s. The Fordson tractor is fitted with Bomford & Evershed half-tracks, jointly designed by Douglas Bomford and A. J. Hosier and introduced in 1944.

234. This Bawden 'one-way' plough, built in Barnstaple in Devon, was one of the first reversible tractor ploughs. The large wheel and lever arrangement behind the driver was used to trip the plough out of work turn it over. The tractor is a 1938 Fordson.

235. Before the preservation movement, the closest a tractor came to a recreational activity was the ploughing match. Britain has a long tradition of ploughing competitions, first with horses and later with tractors. The British Ploughing Association was formed in May 1951 with the first British National Ploughing Contest held the following November. A Scottish competitor ploughs a high-cut furrow with a wartime Massey-Harris Pacemaker tractor.

236. A 1943 Fordson at a local ploughing match with a Ransomes TS43 Motrac. The driver has his sighting poles for marking out his opening split. The Model N Fordson was a popular choice for ploughing matches as its driving position left the plough control levers within easy reach.

Chapter 9: Endless Tracks

237. *Tracklayers were indispensable on heavier land and gave the farmers a greater opportunity to get the work done when conditions were deteriorating. The Clayton crawler, built from 1916 by Clayton & Shuttleworth of Lincoln, was powered by a Dorman petrol engine. The machine in the photograph, taken during the First World War, belonged to the Ministry of Munitions and was operated by a driver from the Motor Transport section of the Army Service Corps.*

Early Crawlers

238. Cletrac crawlers were imported into Britain by H. G. Burford of Regents Street, London. This 1922 12-20 model had Cleveland's own engine and was in production until 1929. A similar machine bought by the author's grandfather was reportedly the first tractor in south Lincolnshire.

239. The Caterpillar Tractor Company of Peoria, Illinois was formed in 1925 and became the world's best-known manufacturer of crawler tractors with a strong following in the UK. This Caterpillar 30 was operated by Ransomes, Sims & Jefferies of Ipswich and was used for testing its larger implements, such as this TD3 six-furrow disc plough on trial in 1933. The tractor had a four-cylinder petrol engine and the side-mounted fuel tank held over 37 gallons.

Roadless Crawlers

240. *Roadless's later work with four-wheel drive tractors has overshadowed its earlier track developments, and the fact that the company was Britain's most prolific crawler manufacturer from the 1920s to the time of the Second World War is often given little recognition. The first successful Roadless crawler was based on the Rushton tractor, and this rare photograph shows one of the prototype machines undergoing trials in the 1929/30 winter.*

241. *This Roadless tracked version of the American Case Model C was introduced in July 1931. It was rated at 29 hp and weighed three tons. Roadless adopted a rubber-jointed track system, known as 'Elastic Girder', for silent running and low maintenance.*

242. A Roadless tracked version of the single-cylinder Marshall 18/30 prepares to go to work with its fuel bowser and a Ransomes cultivator in tow. It was one of two machines supplied to John Allen of Oxford in 1933. Only about four are believed to have been built.

243. The Bristol tractor began life as a Roadless project and was fitted with the company's rubber-jointed tracks. This early version had a British Anzani vee-twin engine and was produced by Bristol Tractors of Willesden from 1933.

1930s Crawlers

244. A 1936 International T-40 TracTracTor ploughing in Lincolnshire. Introduced in 1932, the T-40 and its sister tractor, the TD-40, were the largest crawlers in International Harvester's range at the time. It was powered by a six-cylinder petrol-paraffin engine and had a five-speed transmission.

245. The Caterpillar D7 9G model was introduced in 1936 as the RD7. It had a six-cylinder diesel engine rated at 70 hp and weighed 10 tons. The company was slowly moving over to compression-ignition power units that set new standards of reliability and economy. The D7 in the photograph is working in the Fens with a Ransomes 'Twinwaytrac' balance plough. Caterpillar's UK importers from 1927 to 1936 were Tractor Traders of Westminster.

246. *This Allis-Chalmers Model K was bought new by Toft Farm at Dunchurch in Warwickshire in 1938. Still going strong on the same farm in 1959, it is seen pulling a two-furrow Ransomes Jumbotrac plough. The petrol-paraffin 'K' crawler was based on the Monarch 35, a design inherited from Monarch Tractors after this concern was integrated into the Allis-Chalmers line in 1928.*

1940s Crawlers

247. This International TD-14 was supplied by the Oxfordshire dealer, A. T. Oliver, to the Surrey War Agricultural Executive Committee during the Second World War. It had a four-cylinder diesel engine rated at 64 hp. International's diesel engines were unique in that they were fitted with a carburettor, spark plugs and magneto for quick starting on petrol.

INTERNATIONAL HARVESTER

248. The International TD-18 was one of the largest American crawlers brought into the UK during the 1940s. It was an impressive beast with nearly 100 hp available from its six-cylinder diesel engine. It weighed over 10 tons and had a six-speed transmission.

Opposite: 250. A 1946 Allis-Chalmers HD10 pulling a five-furrow Ransomes TS39 Hexatrac plough near Dowsby in Lincolnshire. The HD10 developed 86 hp from its four-cylinder GM diesel engine.

249. *Allis-Chalmers' big crawler line, the HD series powered by two-stroke diesel engines supplied by General Motors, was introduced in 1940. The three-cylinder HD7 was rated at 54 hp.*

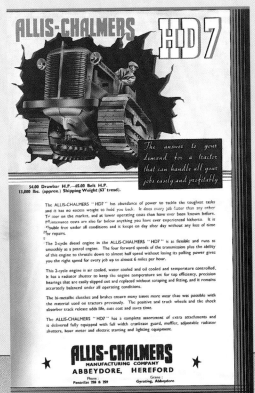

ALLIS-CHALMERS HD7

The answer to your demand for a tractor that can handle all your jobs easily and profitably

54.00 Drawbar H.P.—65.00 Belt H.P.
13,000 lbs. (approx.) Shipping Weight (63" tread).

The ALLIS-CHALMERS "HD7" has abundance of power to tackle the toughest tasks and it has no excess weight to hold you back. It does every job faster than any other Tractor on the market, and at lower operating costs than have ever been known before. Maintenance costs are also far below anything you have ever experienced hitherto. It is trouble free under all conditions and it keeps on day after day without any loss of time for repairs.

The 2-cycle diesel engine in the ALLIS-CHALMERS "HD7" is as flexible and runs as smoothly as a petrol engine. The four forward speeds of the transmission plus the ability of this engine to throttle down to almost half speed without losing its pulling power gives you the right speed for every job up to almost 6 miles per hour.

This 2-cycle engine is air cooled, water cooled and oil cooled and temperature controlled. It has a radiator shutter to keep the engine temperature set for top efficiency, precision bearings that are easily slipped out and replaced without scraping and fitting, and it remains accurately balanced under all operating conditions.

The bi-metallic clutches and brakes ensure many times more wear than was possible with the material used on tractors previously. The positive seal track wheels and the shock absorber track release adds life, cuts cost and saves time.

The ALLIS-CHALMERS "HD7" has a complete assortment of extra attachments and is delivered fully equipped with full width crankcase guard, muffler, adjustable radiator shutters, hour meter and electric starting and lighting equipment.

ALLIS-CHALMERS
MANUFACTURING COMPANY
ABBEYDORE, HEREFORD

Phone:
Pontrilas 258 & 259

Grams:
Gyrating, Abbeydore

Caterpillar Tractors

251. Caterpillar's growing reputation in the UK was enhanced by the superb D2 and D4 models that were introduced in the late-1930s and imported in their hundreds through the 1940s. This 3J model D2 was imported under the Lend-Lease scheme in 1942 for use with the Surrey 'War Ag'. The driver, 'Ven' Dodge, later became Roadless's sales manager.

252. The wide-gauge 5J model D2, seen with a Massey 728 drill, was a popular machine in the Fens for sowing, rolling and spring work. The main four-cylinder Caterpillar diesel engine was started by an auxiliary two-cylinder petrol engine, usually known as the 'donkey engine'.

253. The 'J' model D2s were replaced by the improved Caterpillar 'U' Series with a more powerful engine in 1947. This 1948 D2 4U model has the rear sprocket from an earlier Caterpillar Twenty Two, which has been fitted back-to-front to turn it into a wide-gauge crawler. The plough is a Ransomes Multitrac.

254. A late 7J model Caterpillar D4 in Levertons' yard at Spalding. In addition to being Caterpillar main distributors and providing sales and service for a large part of the country, Levertons also manufactured cabs for the crawlers as seen here and on the previous photograph. This all-steel cab dated from the mid-1950s.

Marshall-Fowler Crawlers

255. *This 1947 FD3 was one of the last of a line of postwar Fowler crawlers that began with the 35 model launched in October 1945. It had a three-cylinder diesel engine designed by the company's development engineer, Arthur Freeman Sanders.*

256. *After John Fowler of Leeds was bought out and merged with Marshalls of Gainsborough in 1946, the former company's crawlers were re-designed to take the single-cylinder two-stroke diesel Marshall power unit. Known as the Fowler VF, the new model was announced in 1947 and put into production the following year.*

257. Fowler's heavy crawler line was represented by the mighty Challengers. This Challenger 3 was an ex-RAF tractor that had been mothballed until it was sold at Ruddington auction in 1962. Unused and as new, it was bought for £650 for use on a farm near Rugby in Warwickshire and is seen ploughing with a four-furrow Ransomes Marquis.

258. The VF crawler was replaced by the Track-Marshall in 1956. A line of the more powerful 55 models, introduced in 1959 and fitted with Perkins 4.270 diesel engines, await delivery at Fenton & Townsend's premises in Sleaford.

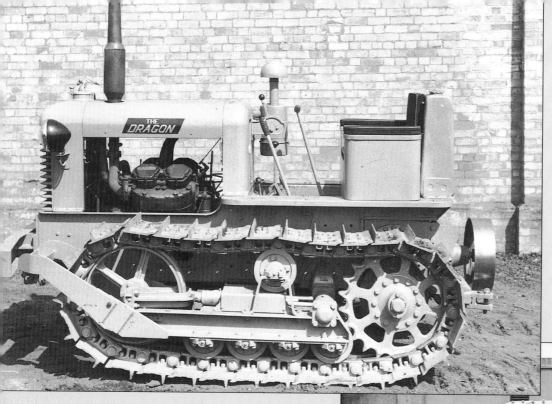

British Crawlers

259. This Loyd Dragon was one of the lesser-known makes of British crawlers that appeared on the postwar market. Launched in 1950, it was built by Vivian Loyd, the designer of the wartime Bren-gun carrier, and built at Camberley in Surrey. The tractor shown was fitted with a Turner V4 diesel engine, but a Dorman 4DS was optional. Few were sold, and the crawler disappeared into obscurity in less than two years.

260. The British tank and armaments manufacturer, Vickers-Armstrong Ltd., introduced its Vigor and Vikon heavy crawlers during the 1950s. Prior to that, the company had built this Shervick prototype crawler based on Sherman tank running gear. Designed for military use and the ground nut scheme, it remained on the secret list and was never released for production.

261. *A Track-Marshall 55 from Gainsborough is followed by an International BTD-6 from Doncaster, both using International drills to sow spring barley at Kites Hardwick, near Rugby, in the 1960s.*

1960s Crawlers

262. A Fiat 70C on demonstration with a Ransomes TS69 Hexatrac plough in 1963. The Italian crawlers were sold in Britain by Mackay Industrial Equipment of Feltham in Middlesex until the company set up its own agency, Fiat Motors Ltd. in 1967. The 70C had a four-cylinder diesel engine with electric or donkey-engine start and cost £3,995.

TRACTORS FIAT LIMITED

263. The Track-Marshall crawler range was uprated with the introduction of the six-cylinder 70 model in 1961. Seen with a seven-furrow Kverneland plough, it had the benefit of 70 bhp from its Perkins 6.354 engine.

264. The 17A model Caterpillar D7 Series C was built from 1955 to 1961. This 1958 example was a 140 hp tractor with a turbocharged version of the four-cylinder engine. It is fitted with a Marshall toolbar and a three-leg Ransomes subsoiler.

265. The Caterpillar product line continued to expand, and a number of D4 and D4C tractors were manufactured in the UK at a plant in Glasgow from 1956. This 82A model D6C was in production from 1964 to 1967. It had a six-cylinder engine with a low-pressure turbocharger and developed over 120 hp.

Crawlers in Decline

266. *By the 1980s, tracks were becoming unfashionable; the crawler was losing ground to the four-wheel drive tractor that offered greater versatility while a succession of several dry summers saw the market for tracklayers shrink even further; a few new models appeared, but many manufacturers were signalling an end to crawler production. This 1979 TD-8CA, rated at 83 bhp, was the last model of International farm crawler to be made at Doncaster.*

267. *The Britannia, launched at the 1983 Royal Show and powered by a 70 hp Perkins 4.236 engine, was one of the last new Track-Marshall crawlers. The company faced changing fortunes and a succession of new owners before falling orders led to an end to crawler production at Gainsborough during the mid-1990s.*

268. If value for money was a consideration, then there was a choice of tracked machines available from Eastern European manufacturers such as Belarus and Universal. The Universal 445C, seen with a Sellar plough at the Long Sutton Tractors at Work demonstration in 1979, was made in Romania by UTB. Based on a Fiat design, it performed well, was priced right and several were sold in Britain.

TRACTORS FIAT LIMITED

269. Fiat of Italy dominated the agricultural crawler market in Europe and claimed to have 50 per cent of world sales. The company had an impressive line of farm crawlers, including this 1355C model that had a 135 hp six-cylinder engine. For a time, it was one of the few large tracklayers available in Britain, with sales handled by the UK subsidiary based at Bury St. Edmunds in Suffolk.

Chapter 10: A New Power in Tractors

270. *The mid-1960s saw the emergence of more modern tractor lines to suit world markets. David Brown changed the colour of its tractors from red to white with the new Selectomatic range that appeared in October 1965. The 990 model, seen with an Allis-Chalmers 505T baler, had a four-cylinder engine developing 55 hp. It cost £954 with the optional twelve-speed transmission.*

The new ranges, often referred to as the second generation of postwar tractors, brought sleeker styling, multiple-speed transmissions and more sophisticated hydraulic systems, as well as greater driver comfort and ergonomic controls. While the most significant new releases of the period were Massey Ferguson's 'Red Giants' and Ford's 6X 'Worldwide' tractors, most of the other major manufacturers were also offering new models.

271. International Harvester updated its models with more power, new styling and new features. The 66 hp 634 model shown was the largest of the Doncaster-built tractors. Launched in December 1968, it cost £1,160 and had draft control hydraulics with lower-link sensing based on a unique torsion-bar design.

272. The Nuffield range gained its final facelift with the 3/45 and 4/65 models, introduced in June 1967, featuring more modern styling and a number of detail changes. The 4/65, seen with a Bamford plough, was rated at 65 hp and had a ten-speed gearbox. The Nuffield name was dropped two years later when the range was re-badged as Leyland tractors with a new blue livery in 1969.

Safety Cabs

273. The Agriculture (Safety Cabs) Regulations introduced in September 1970 required all new tractors sold in the UK after that date to be fitted with an approved cab or frame to protect the driver from overturning accidents. Massey Ferguson's 100 Series, introduced as the 'Red Giants' in 1964, were fitted with the company's flexible-clad safety cabs from 1970. The 75 hp 185 model made its debut in 1971 and is shown with both the standard cab and the 'De-luxe' cab with rigid cladding.

274. John Deere tractors sold in Britain were fitted with safety cabs supplied by Alexander Duncan of Aberdeen. The basic frame structure is seen on this 2120 model with a Massey Ferguson baler. Built at Mannheim in Germany from 1968, the John Deere 2120 had a 72 hp four-cylinder engine, an eight-speed gearbox and a closed-centre hydraulic system.

Opposite: 275. Ford's safety cabs for the UK were designed in Sweden and built by the company's Danish industrial division in Copenhagen with a toughened box-section steel safety frame. The tractor is the 75 hp 5000 model, part of the revamped Ford Force 6Y range launched in 1968. Built at Basildon, it was one of the best-selling British tractors of the time.

Four-Wheel Drive Developments

276. Based on the 6X Ford 5000, this 1967 Roadless Ploughmaster 95 offered increased power and traction with a four-wheel drive axle and a six-cylinder Ford 2703E engine developing 95 bhp. By the mid-1970s, with buoyant home and export markets, the demand for four-wheel drive tractors from Britain's specialist manufacturers was such that there was a two-year waiting list for Roadless tractors.

277. There were nine models in County's four-wheel drive range after the flagship model 1454 was launched in March 1972. Built around an American Ford 9000 skid unit, it had a six-cylinder engine turbocharged to 145 bhp and cost £6,600.

278. Although better known for its Ford conversions, County also designed and built equal-size four-wheel drive tractors for both International Harvester and Leyland. This County version of the International 634 was sold as the 634 'All-Wheel Drive' to differentiate from a Roadless version that was known as the 634 'Four-Wheel Drive'. A batch of fifty was made between 1969 and 1972 during which time the tractor's price rose from £2,540 to £3,203.

279. Four Wheel Traction Ltd. of London built a number of four-wheel drive conversions for Massey Ferguson tractors using Selene parts before also turning its attentions to Leyland machines in 1971. The FWT 470 was Four Wheel Traction's conversion of the 70 hp Leyland 270 and is seen on the company's stand at the 1973 Royal Show.

280. On 1 January 1973, Britain became part of the European Economic Community – a move that was reflected in the number of European makes of tractor that were now to be found on the UK market. German Fendt tractors were imported by Bill Bennett Engineering of Chipping Sodbury near Bristol. This Favorit 612S model, seen at the 1973 Royal Show, boasted 130 hp from its six-cylinder engine. Four-wheel drive was standard, as was the manufacturer's unique 'Turbomatik' transmission with a turbo-clutch drive and a sixteen-forward and seven-reverse speed gearbox.

EEC Tractors

281. Watveare Overseas Ltd. handled sales of German Deutz tractors in the UK from a base at Westbury, Wiltshire. The Intrac 2003A was one of the first 'systems' tractors. It was designed for front or rear operations and combined a load-carrying platform for mounting spraying or fertilising attachments.

282. The harvesting machinery manufacturer, A.C. Bamlett Ltd. of Thirsk in Yorkshire, turned concessionaire after it started importing the Italian Same range of tractors into the UK. The six-cylinder air-cooled Drago, seen at the centre of the company's stand at the 1972 Royal Show, was rated at 98 hp and cost £4,495. Same offered four-wheel drive machines at an affordable price and were able to steal sales from the established British manufacturers such as County and Roadless.

283. Fiat offered seven different wheeled tractors in Britain during the mid-1970s. All the models were available with the option of four-wheel drive. The 1000DT was introduced in 1973 and had a 110 hp engine and a twelve-speed gearbox for £4,380.

East European Tractors

The 1970s saw an influx of machines from Eastern Europe and the former Communist Bloc countries arrive on Britain's shores. These tractors from behind the iron curtain were often lacking in refinement with dated technology when compared to their western counterparts, but were rugged and reliable and offered good value for money.

284. Sales of the Polish Agripol Ursus were handled in the UK by Maulden Engineering of Bedfordshire. This 1973 Ursus 335 had a twin-cylinder 35 hp engine, a six-speed gearbox and a range of extras, including its own tool kit, for just £962.

285. The Czechoslovakian Zetor tractor had been available in Britain since 1965 when the 'Unified' series of tractors from the state plant in Brno was imported by Skoda. This Crystal 8011 was part of the second 'Unified' series produced in collaboration with Ursus. It had an 85 hp four-cylinder engine and an 8x4 gearbox with a torque multiplier that doubled it up to a 16x8 transmission. The 1974 model shown cost £2,875.

286. The former Soviet Union was the largest tractor-producing nation in the world and its Minsk plant in the state of Belarus was the largest single manufacturer. Belarus tractors from Minsk were imported into the UK by the Soviet-American trade company, Satra, based in Surrey, from 1967. The MTZ-52 Super model, seen at the 1973 East of England Show, was best summed up by the company's slogan 'The toughest bargain you can drive'. It was a very basic 75 hp tractor, but at £1,545 with four-wheel drive, it was nearly half the price of an equivalent two-wheel drive Ford 5000.

287. Great interest is shown in the Belarus DT75 crawler at its first UK appearance in 1973. Built at the Volgograd plant, the Russian machine had a 100 hp engine and running gear originally designed for a Soviet artillery tractor. It cost £5,600 and around 200 were imported. The same cab was also used on Russian military vehicles.

American Muscle

288. *Few high horsepower tractors were produced in Britain, and the top end of several manufacturers' lines were supplemented by importing more powerful models from the USA. The American John Deere 4020 was available in the UK from 1964 to 1972. Rated at 106 hp, it had a choice of synchromesh or powershift transmissions, and was later joined by the 143 hp 5020 model.*

289. *The International 966 Farmall had a six-cylinder engine delivering 116 hp and an eight-speed gearbox. Manufactured in the USA at International Harvester's Farmall Plant in Illinois, it was imported into the UK from 1972 to 1974, priced at £4,880.*

290. The American White Farm Equipment Company of Illinois was established in 1969 from an amalgamation of the Cockshutt, Oliver and Minneapolis-Moline brands. A few White tractors were brought into the UK by Maulden Engineering, and this 2-150 model, seen at the 1973 Royal Show, had 145 pto hp on tap from its 9.6 litre six-cylinder engine.

291. The 92 hp Massey Ferguson 595 tractor had North American lineage but was made in France at the Beauvais plant. Designed with input from the company's Advanced Engineering and North American Operations divisions in Detroit, it appeared in 1974 and was the precursor of the 500 Series that was introduced at Banner Lane two years later. It cost £6,398 in the UK, and is seen in the company of 100 Series tractors at the East of England Show in 1976.

Quiet Cabs

292. UK noise regulations for agricultural tractor cabs, introduced on 1 June 1976, limited the maximum permitted noise levels inside the cab to 90 decibels. Some manufacturers, such as Massey Ferguson, took this as an opportunity to introduce completely new ranges. The 500 Series featured new cabs, new styling and improvements to the engine, transmission and hydraulics. The 575, seen at a dealer launch held by Norths of Stamford, was the 70 hp model in the range.

293. David Brown simply redesigned its safety cab, raising the floor, fitting sound-deadening materials and mounting it on rubber blocks. From 1979 the company offered this 'De-Luxe' Q-cab, made by Sekura of Denmark, as seen on a 1412 tractor - the top model in the range with a 91 hp turbocharged engine and the company's Hydra-Shift semi-automatic transmission.

294. Leyland's Q-cab had sound-insulated side panels and was mounted on rubber bushes to reduce vibration. Its introduction in 1976 followed a facelift for the tractor range with a new silver hood stripe. A further revamp of the Leyland line in 1979 saw the tractors fitted with a new synchromesh gearbox developed in conjunction with Turner of Wolverhampton. The 285 Synchro model, seen at the 1979 Royal Show, had the six-cylinder 6-98 engine developing 85 bhp.

295. The most stylish of the new Q-cabs was Fiat's Supercomfort cab, introduced for its 80 Series tractors in 1978. It was designed in Italy by Pininfarina – a name more usually associated with exotic sportscar styling – and featured ergonomic controls and very low noise levels. It is seen on Fiat's flagship model, the four-wheel drive 1880DT with a six-cylinder engine turbocharged to 180 hp, ploughing in the UK with a seven-furrow Dowdeswell.

Power Farming

The second half of the 1970s saw a buoyant UK tractor market sustained by a growth in farm incomes, and most manufacturers reported record sales for 1976 and 1977. By 1978, there were over 40,000 tractors in England and Wales, and most operations in both the arable and grassland sectors of the British farming industry were fully mechanised.

296. A Zetor Crystal 8011 with a Bamford forage harvester in Derbyshire.

297. A Roadless 98 with a Class forage harvester at the National Grassland Demonstration in June 1978. The 98 was based on the Ford 7600 skid unit and had a planetary four-wheel drive axle. Roadless's J-Series Q-cab was made by Lambourn Engineering of Berkshire.

298. *Ford's 7A2 range, launched in 1976, was fitted with Q-cabs developed in the USA but built in Britain by GKN Sankey. The 4600 model, seen working with a Ransomes beet harvester, had a 62 bhp three-cylinder engine. Ford had been the UK market leader since 1973, and 1977 was its best ever year for sales.*

Giants of the Field

299. The 'big wheelers' and articulated giants that appeared during the late-1970s were designed more for the North American prairies, but a number were imported into Britain for the larger arable farms. The American Case tractors were sold in the UK through David Brown, as both companies were affiliates of the same parent Tenneco Corporation. The 4890 was a crab-steer machine with a rigid chassis and a 273 hp six-cylinder turbocharged engine.

300. The International 3388, seen on demonstration in September 1979, was the only model from the company's 2+2 Series of articulated tractors to be brought into the UK. Dubbed 'Snoopy' because of its distinctive shape, it had a six-cylinder engine turbocharged to 180 hp.

301. *Steiger of Fargo in North Dakota was one of the most respected manufacturers of articulated four-wheel drive machines and its big tractor line dated back to 1957. Sales in the UK were handled by Offchurch Tractors of Leamington Spa. This Steiger Panther ST325, seen at the 1979 Tractors at Work demonstration with a ten-furrow Dowdeswell plough, had over 300 hp available from its turbocharged Caterpillar 3406-T engine and cost £40,910.*

302. *Not all the four-wheel drive giants were produced in North America. This 240 hp Schluter Super 3500TVL was built at Munich in Germany and sold in the UK through Reco-Schlutrac Ltd. of Huntingdon. It had a massive eight-cylinder 320 hp engine matched by an equally massive price tag of £67,950.*

Chapter 11: Modern Tractor Technology

303. *The 1980s heralded a new age in tractor design with new concepts, advanced features and the accent on driver comfort for increased productivity. Ford's new family of big tractors, the TW Series was launched in 1979. The 195 bhp TW-35, seen with a Claas forage harvester, was the new flagship model following a 1983 upgrade of the range.*

304. Massey Ferguson's 500 Series was replaced by the 600 Series in 1981. Jointly produced at Banner Lane and Beauvais, the new range featured improved flat-floor cabs with lower noise levels and better heating and ventilation. The 698 had the Perkins A4.3182 engine and was a 92 hp tractor.

305. International claimed to offer the 'height of luxury' with its XL Control Centre cabs, introduced with the 85 Series tractors in 1981. The 885XL, shown working with a Bamford forage harvester, must rate as one of the best 'all-rounders' to come out of the Doncaster plant; a compact machine with plenty of reserves of power from its 85 hp engine.

Big Tackle

306. *The new breed in tractors was matched by a new generation of big farm equipment with a greater capacity to get the work done. A Fiat 120C crawler stirs the dust with a set of heavy disc harrows covering eight metres in one pass. The 120C had a six-cylinder engine rated at 120 hp.*

307. *A John Deere 3650 in the hands of a Berkshire contractor powers away with a Claas Quadrant 1200 big square baler. Built at Mannheim in Germany from 1987, the six-cylinder 3650 was turbocharged to 118 hp.*

308. One-pass cultivation and drilling – a Ford 8730 with an Overum Tive pneumatic seed drill and a front-mounted Simba seedbed cultivator. The Ford Series 30 tractors replaced the TW Series in 1989 and had fully-powershift transmissions giving 18x9 speeds. The 163 bhp 8730 was the mid-range model in the line-up of three new tractors.

Big Ploughs

Opposite 309. *The growth in tractor horsepower saw a move towards increasingly larger multi-furrow ploughs. The 'push-pull' concept was a trend favoured for a short time during the mid-1980s by some manufacturers, such as Ransomes with this TSR 300 Series reversible plough. The tractor is the six-cylinder 7810 model from Ford's Generation III range of 1989.*

310. *Dowdeswell Engineering of Rugby specialised in ploughs for big tractors; an eight-furrow DP2 model, a heavy-duty semi-mounted reversible plough, is seen behind a 280 bhp articulated tractor that was made in Canada by Versatile but marketed in the UK by Fiat in its own livery as the 44-28 model.*

311. *A pair of German eight-furrow Rabewerk ploughs behind John Deere and Fiat tractors. Eight-furrows was about the limit for solid-beam ploughs, and later, larger ploughs from manufacturers such as Kverneland and Huard were articulated for greater manoeuvrability.*

The Big Four

While the tractor industry underwent a period of rationalisation caused by depressed sales and a worldwide recession in agriculture, the big four names, Ford, Case IH, Massey Ferguson and John Deere, remained the market leaders in the UK as the country moved into the last decade of the millenium.

312. Seen in its working clothes with a Maschio power harrow, this Ford 7740 was part of the Series 40 range introduced in 1991, by which time the company's tractor operations were under Fiat ownership. The 7740 was powered by a 95 hp turbocharged four-cylinder from the new Genesis family of engines with lower exhaust emissions.

313. Massey Ferguson's 3000 Series was launched in 1986 with Datatronic versions featuring on-board computer systems. The 137 bhp 3125 model joined the range in 1990 and had a turbocharged six-cylinder engine from the cleaner burning Perkins 1000 Series. Massey Ferguson became part of the giant American conglomerate, AGCO, in 1994.

314. By 1990, John Deere could justifiably claim to be the world's largest agricultural machinery manufacturer with global manufacturing and marketing facilities. UK sales were handled through the British subsidiary at Langar in Nottinghamshire.

The 4455 tractor was a big beast; built at the Waterloo plant in the USA from 1989, it had 160 hp under the hood and a host of new features including electronic monitoring systems.

315. Case IH, formed from a merger of the International, Case and David Brown brands in 1985, unveiled its new Magnum line of four big tractors in 1989. Although built in the USA, the Magnum range had a great impact in the UK, offering new levels of power in a compact rigid chassis. This 7130 model, working near Rugby in Warwickshire with a nine-furrow Dowdeswell plough in 1995, was rated at 213 hp.

European Technology

Mergers, takeovers and bankruptcies had seen many famous names disappear, but there were still over twenty-five different brands of tractor on the UK market in 1990, including several European makes.

316. Fendt tractors were expensive but always incorporated the latest technology and were built to last with German precision engineering. The 1988 Farmer 312LSA model had a 127 hp six-cylinder engine and a 21x6 transmission with a 40 kph road speed. Fendt was bought by AGCO in 1997.

317. A 90 hp Valmet 705-4 is put through its paces at a UK demonstration in 1988. The Valmet range, built in Finland and launched in 1982, was the result of co-operation between the Swedish Volvo BM and Finnish Valmet corporations. Although red was Valmet's basic colour, the customer was offered the choice of four other finishes including blue.

318. Deutz launched its Agrostar range with increased levels of in-cab comfort in 1990. The DX6.31 model had an air-cooled six-cylinder engine that was turbocharged to give 120 hp. There was a choice of transmissions with a 48x12 gearbox available. Deutz became part of the Italian Same group, joining Lamborghini and Hurliman, in 1995.

319. Although a few Renault tractors were exhibited in Britain during the 1950s, the French company did not establish a UK base until 1977 when it opened premises at Shipston-on-Stour in Warwickshire and began importing tractors into Southampton by cross-channel ferry from Le Havre. The 155-54 Nectra, seen with a Reco Mengele forage harvester, was a special high-specification model launched in 1991 with a 160 hp engine, a 24x8 powershift transmission and a suspended cab with electronic instrumentation.

The Clash of the Titans

320. *The 1990s saw the emergence of a new generation of technically advanced high-horsepower tractors, designed to cope with the increasingly large cultivation equipment. It was a concept that was first embodied in the Case Magnum range, and one of the original 7100 Series tractors is seen here in the company of a new 276 hp flagship model 7250 tractor preparing land for spring beans in Warwickshire in 1998.*

321. *The Titan Series was Same's flagship range, featuring six-cylinder engines that were both turbocharged and intercooled with electronic speed control. The 145 model is seen working with an Accord drill and Kuhn power harrow combination near Rugby in October 1995.*

322. New Holland's 'Gamma Alta' family of high-horsepower tractors, introduced in 1994, was the company's first integrated tractor range. Available in blue as the Ford Series 70 or in terracotta as the identical Fiat G Series, they were very sophisticated machines with programmable powershift transmissions and a revolutionary 'SuperSteer' front axle. The Fiat G210, seen working above the white cliffs of Dover with Simba discs, had a turbocharged and intercooled six-cylinder engine developing 210 hp.

323. John Deere claimed that its 8000 Series, launched in the UK in October 1994, were the most advanced high-horsepower tractors ever developed, and even patented the design concept. The range featured new engines, transmissions, cabs and controls. The 260 hp flagship model 8400 had an eight-litre six-cylinder engine and a 16x5 powershift transmission.

New Concepts

324. *Towards the end of the twentieth century, several manufacturers began to challenge the established design of the tractor with new ideas and new concepts. JCB launched its 'high-mobility' design for high-speed tractors with full suspension systems at the 1990 Smithfield Show. This 185-65 tractor was the most powerful model in the 1997 Fastrac range and had a six-cylinder turbocharged and intercooled Cummins engine developing 170 hp.*

325. *In 1988, Caterpillar reinvented the agricultural crawler and gave it a new lease of life with its Challenger machines fitted with rubber-belt tracks for greater mobility. A marketing agreement between Caterpillar and Claas of Germany saw the latter company handle the UK and European sales for the Challenger crawlers from 1997. The 410 hp Claas Challenger 95E model is seen working in the UK in 1999.*

326. John Deere followed Caterpillar's lead and introduced its own range of rubber-tracked crawlers, based on the 8000 Series tractors, in 1997. November 1999 saw the launch of the new John Deere 8010T Series of tracked tractors with automatic powershift transmissions and implement management systems as standard. The 8410T model had an 8.1 litre PowerTech engine generating 270 hp.

327. In 1996, Case IH's engineers combined rubber-track technology with big tractor performance by introducing its Quadtrac range. These remarkable machines were based on the company's Steiger family of articulated giants with their wheels replaced by four independent track units for greater flotation and optimum weight distribution. This STX440 model from the latest STX Series Quadtrac range unveiled in the year 2000 has 440 hp available from its 15 litre Cummins QSX15 engine.

British Tractor Plants

328. By the end of the twentieth century, there were just four major tractor plants still operating in the UK. The oldest of these, AGCO's facility at Banner Lane in Coventry, had been building tractors since 1946. Covering over 1.8 million sq ft, the plant is home to Massey Ferguson production, but also builds machines in White and Agco-Allis livery for North America. A 75 hp Massey Ferguson 4235 model is seen on the main assembly line in 1999.

329. JCB Landpower established its factory at Cheadle in Staffordshire to manufacture Fastrac tractors and agricultural machines in 1991. This shot of the Fastrac production line shows some of the latest machines under construction. In 1999, the Fastrac range consisted of six models from 115 to 170 hp.

330. *A Case MX Maxxum on the assembly line at the Wheatley Hall plant in Doncaster in July 1999. After undergoing a £10 million refit in 1996, the factory became the Case Corporation's main European assembly centre for tractors. Following a merger between New Holland and Case, the plant was sold to the Italian tractor manufacturer, Landini, in December 2000.*

331. *Current New Holland TS and TM models on the production line at Basildon in 1999. Recent investment at the Essex plant has seen the facility confirmed as New Holland's main tractor manufacturing centre, producing machines for global distribution. The plant also builds engines for a variety of applications, but sources drivelines and transmissions from Antwerp or Modena.*

Tractors for the 21st Century

The new tractors for the new millennium, launched in 1999, were hi-tech machines, with cab levelling, electronic diagnostic systems and stepless transmissions being the latest buzzwords. However, the future for the manufacturers remained uncertain as sales were falling with British farmers, in particular, facing one of the worst recessions for several decades.

332. Built at Banner Lane, the Massey Ferguson 4270 offered the latest refinements and levels of operator comfort with 110 hp available from its advanced '1006 series' six-cylinder Perkins engine.

333. John Deere introduced two new big green giants into the UK in September 1999. The 9300 had a 12.5 litre engine developing 360 hp and a 24-speed synchronised transmission. Its sister model, the 425 hp 9400, was the most powerful John Deere ever produced.

334. New Holland's impressive Series TM was probably the last new British-built tractor to be introduced before the twentieth century came to a close. Launched in November 1999, the range featured several transmission options, the 'SuperSteer' front axle and 7.5 litre PowerStar engines. The TM165 was a 160 hp tractor and the flagship model in the range.

335. From the same CNH stable came the mighty Case MX Magnums, unveiled in the UK at the end of 1998, offering high levels of comfort, sophistication and specification. The MX270, seen with a Dowdeswell plough, was an outstanding machine with good weight distribution, an excellent turning circle and a six-cylinder turbocharged engine with an electronically-controlled fuel injection system that pushed out over 300 hp.

Picture Credits

Geoff Adamson: 46, 51, 114, 115, 116, 117, 158, 179, 181, 182, 219.

AGCO: 78, 273, 304, 328, 332.

Peter Anderson: 183, 200.

James Baldwin: 279, 280, 281, 282, 284, 285, 286, 287, 289, 290, 291, 292, 294.

David Bate Archives: 168.

Bim Bellamy: 176, 258.

Stephen Burtt: 44, 91, 102, 128, 140, 195, 201, 224, 250, 252, 264, 288.

Arthur Carter: 160, 245.

Case United Kingdom: 72, 86, 87, 88, 89, 271, 278, 327, 335.

Claas UK: 325.

Martin Cole: 198, 304.

Robert Crawford: 35, 48, 171, 172, 173, 174, 175, 191.

Trevor Crawford: 203, 217.

Ven Dodge: 50, 52, 73, 74, 90, 92, 204, 205, 213, 233, 234, 238, 240, 241, 243, 247, 251, 276, 297.

Ernest Doe & Sons Ltd: 177.

Fred Dyer: 239.

Morris Eglen: 66, 67, 77, 105.

Mark Farmer: 53, 54, 57, 58, 59, 60, 61, 62, 65, 68, 69, 70, 226.

John Glanfield: 4, 6, 28, 29, 169, 170.

Bob Houldershaw: 202, 254, 265.

JCB Landpower: 324, 329.

John Deere: 323, 326, 333.

Lilian Ream Exhibition Gallery: 178.

Lincolnshire Free Press & Spalding Guardian: 1, 2, 79, 81, 85, 96, 100, 101, 104, 106, 107, 108, 109, 110, 112, 120, 122, 123, 124, 125, 130, 131, 132, 133, 134, 136, 137, 139, 141, 147, 184, 185, 186, 187, 188, 189, 190, 192, 193, 194, 196, 197, 206, 207, 209, 210, 211, 218, 222, 229, 230, 231, 232, 236, 248, 253, 256.

Peter Love: 5.

Alan Mole Collection: 8, 9, 10, 11, 12, 16, 24, 151.

New Holland UK: 118, 121, 145, 161, 269, 275, 283, 295, 298, 303, 306, 308, 309, 310, 322, 330, 334.

Perkins Engines: 75, 80, 111, 113, 119, 127, 135, 143, 159, 162.

Quadrant Picture Library: 20, 36, 37, 38, 39, 40, 41, 43, 129, 153, 154, 155, 156, 157.

Renault Agriculture: 319.

Jim Russell: Frontispiece, 144, 225, 246, 257, 261, 315, 320, 321.

Ben Serjeant; 235.

Silsoe Research Institute: 93, 94, 95, 97, 99, 142, 199, 221, 259.

Eric Sixsmith Collection: 13, 14, 15.

John Suckling Collection: 208, 262.

Tractor & Machinery: 330.

David Woods: 55, 56.

 **Japonica Press** # Look out for these additional books from Japonica Press

A World-Wide Guide to Massey Ferguson Industrial and Construction Equipment - John Farnworth

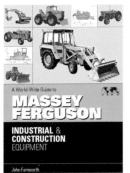

A much needed reference text on this long neglected subject. The book is particularly timely given that MF badging of industrial machines ended in 1997.

It will come as a surprise to many construction equipment enthusiasts that the book identifies an incredible 26 basic types of industrial equipment which were produced and marketed by MF. The book has been prepared as a result of extensive research over the past three years involving contact with specialists in UK, America, Europe, Australia, South Africa and Brazil.

Additionally there are three valuable supporting chapters on early industrial equipment (pre-1964 Massey-Harris, Ferguson and early Massey Ferguson), a chronology of the development of MF's factories production of industrial equipment, and a short history of the development of shuttle transmissions.

The book will provide a valuable reference text and identification guide for industrial equipment enthusiasts, all those interested in the general history of Massey Ferguson and most especially the growing band of Massey Ferguson Industrial equipment collectors world wide. 09540222 0 3

"Ultimate Tractor Power – Articulated Tractors of the World Volume 2, M-Z" - Peter D. Simpson

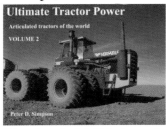

The culmination of over two years of intense research by the author, this fascinating and detailed book pays tribute to large four-wheeled drive articulated tractors from around the world.

With best selling Volume 1 covering A-L, this book covers the remainder of the alphabet. Examines special conversions of these big tractors from wheels to rubber tracks. Also features more one off's built on the farm, with a section on four-wheeled drive articulated scale model tractors and collecting tractor sales literature.

Includes models from USA, Africa and Australia. Each model series is included along with all individual models within the series. New and exciting photographs are accompanied by authoritative text and specifications for each model, including date of manufacture,

engine make, size and power transmission, type and number of speeds, weight and fuel capacity.

Close contact with the manufacturer has enabled the author to include company history and specifications not covered previously. Volume 2 covers from M to Z and includes, among others, Massey-Ferguson, Mancini, Rite, Steiger, Universal, Versatile, Waltana and Zanello. 0 9540222 3 8

"Ultimate Tractor Power - Articulated Tractors of the World Volume 1, A-L" - Peter D. Simpson

Rarely seen in the UK and Europe these giants of the tractor world are at home on the prairies of the USA and in Africa and Australia. Including models from among others USA, Africa, Australia and Russia, the tractors are presented in alphabetical order. Each model series is included along with all individual models within the series. New and exciting photographs are accompanied by authoritative text and specifications for each model, including date of manufacture, engine make, size and power transmission, type and number of speeds, weight and fuel capacity. Close contact with the manufacturer has enabled the author to include company history and specifications not covered previously. Volume 1 covers from A to L and includes ACO, AGCO, Big Bud, Deutz, Ford, Kharkov to name but a few, also included is a section on prototypes and one offs. 09533737 4 6

"A World-Wide Guide to Massey Harris, Ferguson & Early Massey Ferguson Tractors" - John Farnworth

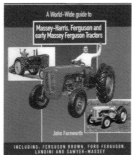

In compiling this world-wide identification guide, John Farnworth has concisely brought together and defined for the first time the extensive tractor family of some 300 models which preceded the Massey Ferguson 100 series tractors launched in 1964. He does this by presenting concise and basic specifications for each model of tractor together with photographs of representative model types. The tractors are grouped in chapters according to their country of manufacture, with the specifications preceding the photographs.

Tractors which are not commonly associated with Massey Ferguson history are also covered. These include Landini tractors manufactured immediately after the take-over by MF, Ford Fergusons and the very early Sawyer Massey steam and Gasoline

engine tractors. These are increasingly becoming recognised as part of Massey Ferguson history and lineage. ISBN 09533737 6 2

"The Big Book Of Farm Tractors" - Robert N.Pripps & Andrew Morland

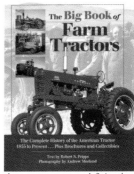

A Lavishly illustrated, complete history of the American tractor 1855 to present.

The Big Book of Farm Tractors is the first large format volume to chronicle the entire history of American farm tractors, from the steam power of the 1850's to current offerings from New Holland, AGCO, John Deere, Caterpillar, and more. Includes detailed descriptions of tractors especially significant to the period, short essays on events defining the times, collectibles, sales memorabilia, old advertisements and photographs.

Though the emphasis is on the American farm tractor this book features many models that were sold within the UK, where many of the photos in the book were actually taken. ISBN 09533737 8 9

"Ultimate John Deere - The History of the Big Green Machines" Ralph W.Saunders

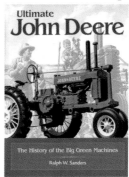

Documents the humble beginnings of John Deere & Company and its evolution as one of the major suppliers of farm equipment in the world. Covers the marvellous machines that provided power to revolutionise farming and help transform the empty prairies of America

Ralph Saunders tells the story of John Deere tractors and of the company's founder. Also includes other pioneers involved in the development of farm implements for the Corn Belt and later John Deere tractors. These important figures include John Deere, his son Charles, engineer Joe Dain and industrial designer Henry Dreyfuss. ISBN 09533737 9 7

"The Ford Tractor Story - Part One: Dearborn to Dagenham 1917-1964" - Stuart Gibbard

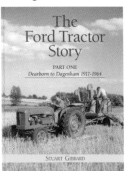

One of the most detailed accounts ever written about Ford Tractor production. Stuart Gibbard's absorbing text is accompanied by a wealth of photographs, many rare and previously unseen. The book follows the development of the Model N, and the E27N to the widely successful E1As and Dextas. A section is also devoted to the American Tractor line.
0 9533737 0 3

"The Ford Tractor Story - Part Two: Basildon to New Holland 1964-today" - Stuart Gibbard

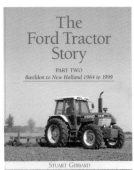

Authoritative text is accompanied by approximately 200 colour and 100 black and white illustrations of both production and prototype tractors. Full account is given of all main Ford and New Holland models, as well as company changes and the personalities involved. An important reference work for anyone connected with the tractor trade, as well as a 'good read' for the general enthusiast. 09533737 1 1

"The Big Book of John Deere Tractors" - Don Macmillan

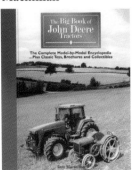

The Ultimate Encyclopedia of John Deere Tractors from around the world. A model by model historical reference to John Deere tractors - including European models - from their beginning until today. Half the book is devoted to the period 1959 up to date, including the recently introduced 9000T tracked tractor. German Lanz and Australian Chamberlain models are covered in depth. Also includes some excellent illustration of rare and original brochures, unique paintings, toys and models. 09533737 2 X

"The Big Book of Caterpillar" - Robert N. Pripps & Andrew Morland

With informative text and stunning photography this is the ultimate encyclopedia of Caterpillar tractors and bulldozers. Includes steam, gas and diesel farm tractors and logging crawlers from the 1860s to the present It covers Cat predecessor companies, Holt, Daniel Best, and C.L.Best as well as discussion of products from associated companies such as Russell Grader, Letourneau and Trackson. 09533737 3 8

"Vintage Allis-Chalmers Tractors" - Lynn Grooms & Chester Peterson Jr.

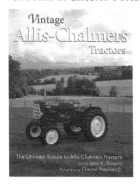

Allis-Chalmers has a rich history, from its beginning as a farm equipment business in 1924 to its rise as the third largest tractor produced in sales 1936, Allis-Chalmers has always been known for its innovation in design, sales and distribution. This publication aimed at collectors, historians and tractor enthusiasts, provides a detailed background along with over 100 spectacular photographs. Covers all models from 1914 on including the Monarch and Advance Rumely models. The authors also discuss Allis-Chalmers in the UK written by Bill Huxley a recognised authority on these famous machines. 09533737 7 0

"Fergusons: The Hunday Experience" - John Moffitt & John Farnworth

John Moffitt is one of the founding fathers of the vintage agricultural equipment movement in the UK. This massive volume brings together in unique style a great deal more information on, and interpretation of Ferguson history, which has evolved out of the creation and presentation of his unique private collection. This beautifully designed book is a must for all Frerguson enthusiasts. 09533737 5 4

**Check with your bookseller or order directly from Japonica Press at: 01377 270209
www.classic-tractors.co.uk**